GCSE English

Macbeth

by William Shakespeare

Studying *Macbeth* can feel like a lot of toil and trouble, but with this amazing CGP Workbook you'll soon know what's what. And which witch is which.

The whole book is bubbling over with practice questions to test your knowledge of the plot, characters, themes, Shakespeare's techniques and more. There's even a handy exam section to help you polish your essay-writing skills!

All in all, it's the perfect way to achieve your GCSE ambitions — just add eye of newt for best results.

The Workbook

Contents

How to Use this Book 1

Section One — Analysis of Acts

Act One 2
Act Two 6
Act Three 8
Act Four 12
Act Five 15
Skills Focus: Using Quotes 18
Skills Focus: P.E.E.D. 19

Section Two — Characters

Macbeth 20
Lady Macbeth 22
Duncan 24
Malcolm and Donalbain 25
Banquo 26
The Macduffs 27
The Witches 28
Other Characters 29
Skills Focus: Making Links 30
Practice Questions 31

Section Three — Context and Themes

Ambition 32
Loyalty and Betrayal 33
Kingship 34
Good and Evil 35
The Supernatural 36
Reality and Appearances 37
Fate and Free Will 38
Skills Focus: Writing about Context 39
Practice Questions 40

Contents

Section Four — Shakespeare's Techniques

Form and Structure of 'Macbeth' ... 41
Mood and Atmosphere ... 43
Poetry in Shakespeare ... 44
Puns and Wordplay ... 45
Imagery and Symbolism ... 46
Skills Focus: Working with Extracts ... 48
Practice Questions ... 49

Section Five — Exam Buster

Understanding the Question ... 50
Making a Rough Plan ... 51
Making Links ... 52
Structuring Your Answer ... 53
Introductions and Conclusions ... 54
Writing about Context ... 55
Linking Ideas and Paragraphs ... 56
Marking Answer Extracts ... 57
Marking a Whole Answer ... 59
Skills Focus: Writing Well ... 61
Practice Questions ... 62

Answers ... 63
The Characters from 'Macbeth'
'Macbeth' Cartoon

Published by CGP

Editors:
Emma Cleasby
Lucy Forsyth
Rose Jones
Louise McEvoy
Liam Neilson
James Summersgill
Rebecca Tate

With thanks to Matt Topping and Nicola Woodfin for the proofreading.
With thanks to Jan Greenway for the copyright research.

Acknowledgements:

Cover Illustration: Glamis Castle (w/c on paper) by Girtin, Thomas (1775-1802) (attr. to) Private Collection/ The Bridgeman Art Library.

With thanks to Rex Features for permission to use the images on pages 1 and 7.

With thanks to ArenaPAL for permission to use the images on pages 3, 10, 12, 20, 24, 25, 27, 29, 34, 36 and 38.

With thanks to Photofest for permission to use the images on pages 5 and 17.

With thanks to John Spurr Photography for permission to use the images on pages 9 and 15.

With thanks to Photostage for permission to use the images on pages 23, 26, 28, 33, 41 and 45.

With thanks to Getty Images for permission to use the images on pages 42 and 47.

ISBN: 978 1 78294 777 6

Printed by Elanders Ltd, Newcastle upon Tyne.

Clipart from Corel®

Based on the classic CGP style created by Richard Parsons.

How to Use this Book

Practise the four main skills you'll need for the exam

Each question tests one or more of the four skills you'll be tested on in the exam. You'll need to:

1) Write about the text in a thoughtful way, picking out appropriate examples and quotations to back up your opinions.
2) Identify and explain features of the play's form, structure and language. Using subject terminology, show how the author uses these to create characters and settings, explore themes and affect the audience's reactions.
3) You'll have to write about the play's context in your exam.
4) Write in a clear, well-structured and accurate way. 5% of the marks in your English Literature GCSE are for spelling, punctuation and grammar.

Use this workbook with or without the CGP Text Guide

1) This workbook is perfect to use with CGP's Text Guide for *Macbeth*. The workbook matches the main sections of the Text Guide, so you can test your knowledge bit by bit.
2) You can also use this book by itself. It covers all the important parts of the text — plot, characters, context, themes and Shakespeare's techniques.
3) The questions refer to the text in detail — you'll need a copy of the play to make the most of the workbook. The line numbers used throughout this book match CGP's Macbeth — The Complete Play.

It prepares you for the exam every step of the way

1) The exam section is jam-packed with useful advice. It guides you through how to tackle the exam, from understanding the questions to building great answers. There's also an easy-to-read mark scheme, which you can use to mark sample answers and improve answers of your own.
2) There are plenty of practice exam questions throughout the book. They give you the opportunity to use what you've revised in each section to write a realistic answer.
3) Exam tips and extra practice exam questions are included in every section. There are also helpful revision tasks designed to get you thinking more creatively. These are marked with stamps.
4) You can find answers to all of the questions and tasks at the back of the book.
5) Each section contains at least one 'Skills Focus' page. These pages help you to practise important skills individually. You can tackle them in any order and prioritise the skills you find the hardest.

You Birnam Wood-n't think a book could hold all of this stuff...

Now you're clued-up on what this lovely book has to offer, it's time to leap head first into some questions. You're not in the exam just yet, so don't panic — just take your time and go through the book at your own pace.

Act One

Act 1, Scene 1 — The Witches plan to meet Macbeth

Q1 Why do you think Shakespeare chooses not to reveal why the Witches want to meet Macbeth?

....

Q2 The Witches say "**Fair is foul, and foul is fair**". What do you think they mean?

....

Q3 Shakespeare begins the play with the Witches. What does this suggest about them?

....

....

Act 1, Scene 2 — King Duncan hears reports of the battle

Q4 Why does Malcolm recognise the Captain?

....

Q5 The Captain describes Macbeth's behaviour in the battle. What impression does the audience get of Macbeth? Use a quote to back up your answer.

....

....

....

Q6 Find a quote from this scene to back up each of these statements.

a) Duncan is impressed with how Macbeth fought in the battle.

....

b) The Captain was harmed in the battle.

....

Act 1, Scene 3 — The Witches make three predictions

Q1 What do the Witches do to the sailor?

....

Q2 Macbeth's first words of the play are "**So foul and fair a day I have not seen.**"
Why are these words significant? What do they suggest about Macbeth?

....

....

....

Q3 Put these events in order by numbering the boxes. The first one has been done for you.

Macbeth orders the Witches to give him more information.	☐
Banquo questions the Witches' physical appearance.	1
The Witches disappear, leaving Banquo and Macbeth confused.	☐
The Witches call Macbeth the Thane of Cawdor and say he will be king.	☐
Banquo asks the Witches to predict his future.	☐

Q4 Read from line 50 to line 87. How do Macbeth and Banquo react to the Witches' predictions?

Macbeth: ....

....

Banquo: ....

....

Q5 Rosse tells Macbeth that he is to become the Thane of Cawdor.
Describe the effect this has on the following things.

a) Macbeth's feelings about the Witches' prophecies

....

....

b) Macbeth's character

....

....

Act 1, Scene 4 — Duncan rewards Macbeth for his loyalty

Q1 Read the paragraph below and fill in the gaps using words from the box.

In this scene, Duncan praises Macbeth and Banquo for their help in the battle and addresses Macbeth as Thane of .... Duncan names his eldest son, ..., heir to the throne, and Macbeth realises that he will need to .... this person before he can become king. Macbeth's .... seems to be taking control of him.

Malcolm	Glamis	ambition	Donalbain	persuade	loyalty	Cawdor	defeat

Q2 Duncan uses a metaphor in this scene when talking about Macbeth's future.
Find a quote which uses this metaphor and explain what it suggests.

Quote: ....

....

Explanation: ....

....

Act 1, Scene 5 — Lady Macbeth decides Duncan must die

Q3 Explain what impression the audience gets of Lady Macbeth in this scene.

....

....

....

....

Q4 What does Lady Macbeth mean in each of the following quotes?

a) "**thy nature, / It is too full o'th'milk of human kindness**"

Meaning: ....

b) "**look like th'innocent flower, / But be the serpent under't**"

Meaning: ....

....

Act 1, Scene 6 — Duncan and the lords arrive at Macbeth's castle

Q1 How does Shakespeare suggest that Duncan feels welcome in Macbeth's castle? Use a quote to support your answer.

© The Weinstein Company/Photofest

....

....

....

....

....

Act 1, Scene 7 — The Macbeths agree to kill Duncan

Q2 Read Macbeth's speech from line 1 to line 27. Decide whether each statement is **true** or **false**, and find a quote to support your answer.

a) Macbeth worries about the consequences of committing murder. **True:** ☐ **False:** ☐

Quote: ....

....

b) Macbeth recognises that he should be protecting Duncan. **True:** ☐ **False:** ☐

Quote: ....

....

c) Macbeth only wants to kill Duncan out of jealousy. **True:** ☐ **False:** ☐

Quote: ....

....

Q3 In your own words, explain how Lady Macbeth convinces Macbeth to kill Duncan.

....

....

....

Milk of human kindness? I'll stick to the orange juice...

Imagine you're Macbeth. Write an entry from his diary describing his experiences in Act 1 and his feelings about them. Explain why he made his decisions and mention anything that influenced him.

Act Two

Act 2, Scene 1 — The famous 'dagger' bit

Q1 How does Shakespeare create a sinister atmosphere at the start of this scene?

....

....

Q2 How does Macbeth react to the vision of the dagger? What does this suggest about him?

....

....

....

....

Act 2, Scene 2 — The deed is done

Q3 Find quotes from this scene which suggest that Macbeth and Lady Macbeth are not as calm as they were in Act 1.

Macbeth: ....

Lady Macbeth: ....

Q4 Read from line 44 to line 57. Describe how Lady Macbeth's behaviour has changed from earlier on in the scene.

....

....

....

Q5 How does Shakespeare show that Macbeth feels guilty about killing Duncan? Use a quote to support your answer.

....

....

....

Act 2, Scene 3 — Duncan's body is discovered

Q1 Put these events in order by numbering the boxes. The first one has been done for you.

Macduff tells Macbeth and Lennox that Duncan has been murdered.	
Macbeth pretends to be shocked by Duncan's murder.	
Macduff goes to wake Duncan up.	
Macduff tells Malcolm that his father is dead.	
Malcolm and Donalbain run away.	
The Porter pretends to be hell's gate-keeper while drunk.	1

Q2 Do you think Lady Macbeth genuinely faints? Explain your answer.

....

....

....

Q3 In your own words, explain why Malcolm and Donalbain fleeing the country could be a good thing for Macbeth.

....

....

Act 2, Scene 4 — Macbeth is about to be made king

Q4 Give an unnatural event that has occurred since Duncan's death. What do events like this suggest about Macbeth's actions?

....

....

....

....

Q5 How can you tell Macduff doesn't trust Macbeth?

....

PRACTICE TASK

Macbeth regretted taking life advice from a dagger...

Write a letter from Malcolm to be sent in secret to his allies in Scotland. You should include a summary of the events that Malcolm has experienced in Act 2, as well as his opinion of Macbeth.

Act Three

Act 3, Scene 1 — Macbeth plots Banquo's murder

Q1 Read from line 1 to line 10. Decide whether each statement is **true** or **false**, and find a short quote to support your answer.

a) Banquo is convinced that the Witches' prophecies are false. **True:** ☐ **False:** ☐

Quote: ....

....

b) Banquo tries not to dwell on the future. **True:** ☐ **False:** ☐

Quote: ....

Q2 Put these events in order by numbering the boxes. The first one has been done for you.

Banquo tells Macbeth that he is loyal to him. ☐
Macbeth suggests Malcolm and Donalbain are to blame for Duncan's murder. ☐
Banquo speaks about Macbeth's rise to power. [1]
Macbeth orders two murderers to kill Banquo. ☐
Macbeth asks Banquo what he plans to do before the feast. ☐
Macbeth says that he thinks Banquo is a threat to him. ☐

Q3 Find a quote from this scene which shows how Macbeth flatters Banquo.

....

Q4 How does Macbeth convince the murderers to kill Banquo? Use a quote to support your answer.

....

....

....

....

Q5 What reason does Macbeth give for having Banquo killed secretly?

....

....

Act 3, Scene 2 — Macbeth decides to act alone

Q1 Why do you think Macbeth refuses to give his wife details of his plan to kill Banquo?

....

....

....

Q2 Find a quote which supports the following statements.

a) Lady Macbeth is unhappy even though she has succeeded in having Duncan killed.

....

b) Now that Macbeth is king, he envies Duncan.

....

Act 3, Scene 3 — Banquo is murdered

Q3 Banquo is murdered in a "***park near the palace***". Why does this make Macbeth seem reckless?

....

....

Q4 Find a quote that shows Banquo is murdered at sunset.
Explain what the sunset suggests about Banquo's murder.

Quote: ....

....

Explanation: ....

....

....

Q5 How does Shakespeare suggest that Macbeth's position as king is insecure?

....

....

Act 3, Scene 4 — Macbeth sees Banquo's ghost

Q1 Put these events in order by numbering the boxes. The first one has been done for you.

Macbeth comments on Banquo's absence from the feast.	
Macbeth hosts a feast for his thanes.	1
Lady Macbeth asks the guests to leave.	
The First Murderer tells Macbeth that Banquo is dead but Fleance escaped.	
Macbeth notices Banquo's ghost, but no one else can see it.	

Q2 Read from line 37 to line 107, then answer the following questions.

a) How does Macbeth react when he sees Banquo's ghost?

....

....

....

b) Why do you think Macbeth reacts in this way?

....

....

Q3 How does Lady Macbeth try to regain control after Macbeth behaves strangely at the banquet?

....

....

....

Q4 Read from line 122 to the end of the scene. Find a quote to back up each of these statements.

© Johan Persson/ArenaPAL

Statement	Quote that shows this
a) Macbeth thinks that his crime might lead to more violence.	
b) Macbeth is keen for more information from the Witches.	
c) Macbeth decides to prioritise his own safety from now on.	

Act 3, Scene 5 — The Witches meet with Hecate

Q1 What is the relationship between Hecate and the Witches like in this scene?

....

....

Q2 What does Hecate plan to do to Macbeth?

....

....

Act 3, Scene 6 — Lennox talks about Macbeth's reign

Q3 In this scene, Lennox and a Lord comment on the state of Scotland. Why do you think Shakespeare uses minor characters like these to criticise Macbeth?

....

....

Q4 How can you tell that Lennox doesn't trust Macbeth? Back up your answer with a quote.

....

....

....

....

Q5 What does the audience learn in this scene about what Malcolm and Macduff are doing in England?

Malcolm: ....

....

Macduff: ....

....

I'd rather fight Banquo's ghost than a rhino to be honest...

Make a flowchart to show how the Witches' prophecies influence events in the play until the end of Act 3. Use arrows and labels to show any connections or links between the events that you identify.

Act Four

Act 4, Scene 1 — Macbeth visits the Witches

Q1 Why do you think Shakespeare chooses to open Act 4 with the Witches' spell?

....

....

Q2 Hecate praises the Witches in this scene. Why has her attitude towards them changed?

....

....

Q3 One witch calls Macbeth "**Something wicked**". What does this suggest about how the audience should view Macbeth?

....

....

....

....

Q4 The Witches make three apparitions appear in front of Macbeth. Complete the table below by summarising what each one says to Macbeth and how he reacts to what they say.

Apparition	What it says to Macbeth	Macbeth's reaction
a) An armoured head without a body		
b) A bloody child		
c) A child wearing a crown and carrying a branch		

Q5 Why does the vision of the kings have such a powerful effect on Macbeth?

....

....

Act 4, Scene 2 — Macbeth has Lady Macduff and her son murdered

Q1 Why might the audience feel tense at the start of this scene?

....

....

Q2 Find a quote to back up each of these statements.

a) Lady Macduff is angry with Macduff for fleeing the country.

Quote: ....

b) Rosse tries to reassure Lady Macduff.

Quote: ....

Q3 Fill in the gaps in the passage below.

Lady Macduff speaks to her son affectionately and calls him "**Poor bird**" and "**poor monkey**". She responds to all of his .... patiently and teaches him about the fate of .... They joke about whether Lady Macduff will replace her .... by visiting the market. The fact that Lady Macduff and her son .... each other like this shows they have a .... relationship.

Q4 How does Lady Macduff react to the messenger's warning? Use a quote to support your answer.

....

....

....

Q5 How does Shakespeare make the murder of Macduff's son seem shocking?

....

....

....

....

Act 4, Scene 3 — Malcolm and Macduff meet

Q1 Put these events in order by numbering the boxes. The first one has been done for you.

Macduff and Malcolm set off to confront Macbeth.	
Macduff learns that his family have been killed in his absence.	
Malcolm reveals that the English have given him an army to fight Macbeth.	
Malcolm and Macduff discuss Macbeth's tyranny.	1
Rosse delivers news of Scotland under Macbeth's reign.	
Malcolm lies to Macduff about how he would behave as a king.	

Q2 Why is Malcolm suspicious of Macduff? Give at least two reasons and use quotes to support your answer.

....

....

....

....

Q3 Identify who said each of these phrases, then explain what each one means.

a) **"good men's lives / Expire before the flowers in their caps"** Said by: ....

Meaning: ....

b) **"Did heaven look on, / And would not take their part?"** Said by: ....

Meaning: ....

c) **"Be this the whetstone of your sword"** Said by: ....

Meaning: ....

Q4 How and why is Macduff's attitude towards Macbeth affected by the news of his family's murder?

....

....

Be this book the whetstone of your revision...

Write a paragraph explaining how Macbeth's character has changed since the beginning of the play. Identify which events have influenced Macbeth and explain how they have affected his character.

Act Five

Act 5, Scene 1 — Lady Macbeth sleepwalks

Q1 How does Shakespeare show that Lady Macbeth has become powerless? Back up your answer with a quote.

....

....

....

....

....

© John Spurr Photography

Q2 Why won't the Gentlewoman reveal to the Doctor what Lady Macbeth has said in her sleep?

....

Q3 The Doctor says that "**Unnatural deeds / Do breed unnatural troubles; infected minds / To their deaf pillows will discharge their secrets.**" What does he mean?

....

....

Act 5, Scene 2 — The thanes prepare for battle

Q4 Why do you think Shakespeare includes a reference to Birnam Wood in this scene?

....

Q5 Decide whether these statements are **true** or **false**, and find a short quote to support your answer.

a) Rumours are spreading about Macbeth. **True:** ☐ **False:** ☐

Quote: ....

b) The thanes believe that Macbeth's position as King is secure. **True:** ☐ **False:** ☐

Quote: ....

....

Act 5, Scenes 3 and 4 — Birnam Wood comes to Dunsinane

Q1 In Scene 3, Macbeth says that he "**cannot taint with fear**" (he won't be afraid). How does Macbeth's behaviour in this scene suggest that this is not true? Give a quote to support your answer.

....

....

....

....

Q2 How does Shakespeare influence the audience's opinion of Macbeth in these scenes?

....

....

....

Q3 Find a quote in Scene 4 that suggests that Macbeth can only be defeated using violence.

....

Act 5, Scene 5 — Lady Macbeth dies

Q4 How does Macbeth react to the news of his wife's death?

....

....

....

Q5 Complete the table below to show how Macbeth's feelings change during this scene.

Quote	What it suggests about Macbeth
	Macbeth is confident of winning the battle.
	Macbeth is starting to doubt the Witches' prophecies.
"I 'gin to be aweary of the sun"	

Act 5, Scenes 6 to 9 — Macbeth is defeated and Malcolm becomes king

Q1 Decide whether each statement is **true** or **false**, and find a quote to support your answer.

a) Malcolm's army advances silently towards Macbeth's castle. **True:** ☐ **False:** ☐

Quote: ....

b) All of Macbeth's soldiers remain loyal to him. **True:** ☐ **False:** ☐

Quote: ....

c) At the start of Scene 8, Macbeth still trusts the Witches' prophecies. **True:** ☐ **False:** ☐

Quote: ....

Q2 Find a quote from Scene 8 which suggests Macbeth has regained some of his honour. Explain how it does this.

Quote: ....

Explanation: ....

Q3 How does Malcolm immediately prove himself to be a worthy king?

Q4 What similarities are there between the ending and the beginning of the play? Use examples to support your answer.

Exciting! A bloody battle, a new king and one Macdeath...

Now you've made it through the play (phew), write down the main events in *Macbeth*. List your events in the order that they happen in the play and include at least three events from each act.

 ☐  ☐  ☐

Using Quotes

In the exam, you'll have to back up your points with quotes from the play. You won't have a copy of the text with you, so it's important to memorise some useful quotes. To really impress the examiner, you'll need to embed your quotes in your sentences so that they sound natural. This means picking out the parts of your quote that are the most relevant to your point and then including them in a sentence to back up that point. Have a go at these questions and you'll get the hang of it in no time.

Q1 Read these statements about quotes.
Decide whether each one is **true** or **false**.

	True	**False**
All your quotes should be written exactly as they appear in the text.	☐	☐
An embedded quote is better than a quote added to the end of a sentence.	☐	☐
Quotes should simply repeat what you have written.	☐	☐
You should include lots of long quotes.	☐	☐
Your quotes don't necessarily need to back up your argument.	☐	☐

Q2 Rewrite the following sentences so that a short part of the quote is embedded in each one.
The first one has been done for you.

Sentence	Quote	New sentence
Macbeth demands that the Witches reveal the source of their prophecies to him.	"Say from whence / You owe this strange intelligence"	Macbeth demands that the Witches reveal the source of their "strange intelligence" to him.
Lady Macbeth says that Macbeth is too much of a coward to kill Duncan.	"yet do I fear thy nature, / It is too full o'th'milk of human kindness / To catch the nearest way."	
Macbeth acted bravely in the battle against the Norwegians.	"Like valour's minion, carved out his passage / Till he faced the slave"	
Lady Macduff thinks her husband's decision to leave was foolish.	"He had none — / His flight was madness."	
Lady Macbeth's nightmares are tormenting her.	"As she is troubled with thick-coming fancies, / That keep her from her rest."	

P.E.E.D.

P.E.E.D. is a great way for you to structure your answers — it makes your paragraphs more concise and analytical. In each of your paragraphs, you need to make a **point**, give a supporting **example**, then **explain** how this example backs up your argument. Finally, to really impress the examiner, you need to **develop** your point by explaining its effect on the audience, or its links to themes, context or other events in the play. Here are a couple of exercises to help you get to grips with P.E.E.D.

Q1 Neither of the sample answers below have used P.E.E.D. correctly. For each, say which stage of P.E.E.D. is missing.

a) Shakespeare presents Duncan as a good king by showing that other characters admire him. Macduff says that Duncan was "a most sainted king" in Act 4, Scene 3. This directly contrasts with Macbeth, who is seen by others as a cruel and tyrannical ruler.

Missing stage: ....

b) Banquo is portrayed as one of the bravest characters in the play. In Act 3, Scene 1, Macbeth states that Banquo has "a wisdom that doth guide his valour". By referring to both Banquo's "wisdom" and "valour", it is implied that other characters recognise Banquo's bravery and admire him for it.

Missing stage: ....

Q2 Fill in the missing steps in the P.E.E.D. structures below.

a) Point: Evil women are often presented as masculine.

Example: The Witches have "beards" but Banquo thinks they "should be women".

Explain: ....

Develop: The ambiguity of their gender mirrors Lady Macbeth's loss of femininity. Like the Witches, Lady Macbeth's evilness has made her appear more masculine.

b) Point: Shakespeare presents Donalbain as a perceptive character.

Example: ....

Explain: This implies that Donalbain is not deceived by Macbeth's false appearances.

Develop: This contrasts with Duncan, who is unable to identify the Macbeths' treachery.

Macbeth

Q1 Find a quote from the play that shows that Macbeth is:

a) brave

Quote: ....

b) merciless

Quote: ....

c) easily influenced

Quote: ....

....

Q2 Read Act 1, Scene 2 and Act 5, Scene 8. Why do you think Shakespeare presents Macbeth as a brave warrior at the start and the end of the play?

....

....

....

Q3 How does Shakespeare show that Macbeth's decision to kill Duncan is not an easy one to make? Use a quote to back up your answer.

....

....

....

....

Q4 Find a quote in Act 3, Scene 1 which suggests that Macbeth is determined to have Banquo killed. Explain how Macbeth's attitude to murder has changed since Act 1.

Quote: ....

Explanation: ....

....

Q5 Decide whether these statements about Macbeth are **true** or **false**.

	True	False
Macbeth stands up to Lady Macbeth. (Act 2, Scene 2)	☐	☐
Macbeth feels secure in his reign once Banquo is dead. (Act 3, Scene 4)	☐	☐
Macbeth vows to act more decisively after seeing the apparitions. (Act 4, Scene 1)	☐	☐
Macbeth doesn't care that Lady Macbeth is unwell. (Act 5, Scene 3)	☐	☐
Macbeth is too scared to surrender to Malcolm. (Act 5, Scene 8)	☐	☐

Q6 In Act 5, Scene 5, Macbeth says that life is "**a walking shadow**" and a "**tale / Told by an idiot**". What does this suggest about Macbeth's character at this point in the play?

....

....

....

....

Q7 Find an example in the play of Macbeth's masculinity being questioned. Explain how this influences his behaviour.

Example: ....

Explanation: ....

....

Q8 What plays a more important role in Macbeth's schemes: Macbeth's ambition or the Witches' prophecies? Give reasons for your answer.

....

....

....

....

....

Macbeth's "vaulting ambition" was handy in gymnastics...

During the play, Macbeth shows impulsiveness, overconfidence and cruelty. Find an example of a time when Macbeth shows each of these character traits and choose a quote to back up your choice.

Lady Macbeth

Q1 Fill in the gaps in the table below. The first one has been done for you.

Event in the play	What it reveals about Lady Macbeth
a) Lady Macbeth convinces Macbeth to kill Duncan.	She can manipulate Macbeth.
b) She alone devises the plot to kill Duncan.	
c) She says that she wouldn't have been able to kill Duncan because he reminded her of her father.	
d) Lady Macbeth covers up Macbeth's unusual behaviour when he sees Banquo's ghost.	
e) Lady Macbeth's suicide takes place offstage.	

Q2 Read Act 1, Scene 5, lines 37-53. How does the language in this passage affect the audience's view of Lady Macbeth? Use a quote to support your answer.

....

....

....

Q3 Summarise what the following quotes mean, then explain what they suggest about Lady Macbeth's feelings about Duncan's murder.

a) "**What cannot you and I perform upon / Th'unguarded Duncan?**"
(Act 1, Scene 7, lines 69-70)

Meaning: ....

Explanation: ....

....

b) "**My hands are of your colour, but I shame / To wear a heart so white.**"
(Act 2, Scene 2, lines 64-65)

Meaning: ....

Explanation: ....

....

Q4 Read Act 3, Scene 2, lines 4-12, then answer the questions below.

a) How does Lady Macbeth's behaviour change when Macbeth arrives? Support your answer with a quote.

b) Why do you think Lady Macbeth's behaviour changes?

Q5 Find two quotes from the text which show Lady Macbeth is a cold-hearted character.

1)

2)

Q6 Briefly summarise how guilt affects Lady Macbeth throughout the play.

© Donald Cooper/Photostage

Q7 Do you think Lady Macbeth is more ambitious or less ambitious than Macbeth? Explain your answer.

Lady Macbeth washed her hands, but she'd lost all soap...

Read Act 5, Scene 1, lines 22-48. **How does Shakespeare present Lady Macbeth's anxiety and fear in *Macbeth*?** You should refer to the extract above and to the play as a whole in your answer.

Duncan

Q1 Decide whether each statement is **true** or **false**, and find a quote to back up your answer.

a) Duncan feels that he owes something to Macbeth. **True:** ☐ **False:** ☐

Quote: ....

b) Duncan thinks it's easy to judge whether people are honest. **True:** ☐ **False:** ☐

Quote: ....

Q2 Give three quotes from the text that show that Duncan is a respected king.

1) ....

2) ....

3) ....

Q3 Why might Duncan be considered a fatherly figure to his men? Give a reason for your answer.

....

Q4 How does Duncan's language suggest that he is an honourable king? Give a quote from the play to support your answer.

....

© Johan Persson/ArenaPAL

Who can survive as a Scottish monarch? Duncan't...

Shakespeare presents Duncan as a good king, but he still has flaws. Write a short paragraph giving two examples of times when Duncan misplaces trust in others and explain the effect each one has.

Malcolm and Donalbain

Q1 Explain what Donalbain means when he says "**Where we are, / There's daggers in men's smiles**" (Act 2, Scene 3, lines 133-134).

Q2 Malcolm and Donalbain decide to flee Scotland after Duncan's murder. Give an advantage and a disadvantage of this decision for them.

Advantage:

Disadvantage:

Q3 How does Shakespeare use the battle in Act 5 to show that Malcolm is a good military leader? Explain your answer.

Q4 Make a short comparison of Malcolm and Duncan, looking at their similarities and differences.

Donalbain ran to Ireland and waited for it all to blow over...

In Act 4, Scene 3, Malcolm describes the qualities of a good king. Think about how Malcolm's behaviour at different points in the play can be linked with the qualities he highlights in this speech.

Banquo

Q1 Briefly describe an event in the play where Banquo demonstrates each of these qualities.

a) Honour

b) Wisdom

Q2 How can you tell that Banquo is ambitious? Use a quote to support your answer.

© JDonald Cooper/Photostage

Q3 In Act 3, Scene 4, Banquo's ghost sits in Macbeth's place at the table. Why is this significant?

Q4 Banquo and Macbeth share some character traits, but they choose to act differently. How does this affect the audience's opinion of Banquo?

Banquo's "gory locks" started a new trend in ghostland...

Imagine that you're interviewing Banquo's ghost. Write three questions that you'd ask him about his experiences from his meeting with the Witches onwards. Write down the answers that he might give.

The Macduffs

Q1 Fill in the gaps in the table below. The first one has been done for you.

Event in the play	What it suggests about the Macduffs
a) Macduff doesn't attend Macbeth's coronation.	Macduff is suspicious of Macbeth.
b) Macduff asks Malcolm to help defeat Macbeth and his brutal rule in Scotland.	
c) Lady Macduff stands up to the murderers when they ask her where her husband is.	

Q2 In Act 4, Scene 3, Macduff refuses to support Malcolm when he pretends that he would be a worse king than Macbeth. What does this suggest about Macduff?

....

....

Q3 How does Shakespeare show that Macduff's son dies bravely? Support your answer with a quote.

....

....

....

Q4 Write a short comparison of Macduff and Macbeth, giving examples from the play to support your answer.

....

....

....

....

....

Macduff regretted counting his "pretty chickens"...

Some people think that Macduff does the right thing when he puts his country before his family in order to save all of Scotland. Do you agree with this view? Write a paragraph explaining your answer.

The Witches

Q1 Find a quote from the play which suggests that the Witches are:

a) wicked

Quote: ....

b) supernatural

Quote: ....

c) able to predict the future

Quote: ....

Q2 Why do you think Shakespeare gives the Witches beards?

....

....

Q3 Read Act 3, Scene 5. What does Hecate's language suggest about her to the audience? Support your answer with a quote.

....

....

....

Q4 The Witches meet on a heath (an open area of land where very little grows) in Acts 1 and 3. What does this setting suggest about them?

....

....

....

....

© JDonald Cooper/Photostage

Never get between a witch and a pile of chestnuts...

Read Act 4, Scene 1, lines 35-60. Write an essay plan for this question: **How is the Witches' behaviour presented by Shakespeare in this extract and in the rest of the play?** Make sure to back up your points with evidence and include examples from the extract and the play as a whole in your plan.

Other Characters

Q1 The Porter in Macbeth's castle pretends to be hell's gate-keeper in Act 2, Scene 3. What does this suggest to the audience about Macbeth?

....

....

Q2 Why do you think Shakespeare includes a comic character like the Porter at this point in the play?

....

....

....

....

Q3 Answer each question and then choose a quote from the text to support your answer.

a) How does Rosse feel about Macbeth's rule in Act 4, Scene 3?

....

....

Quote: ....

b) In Act 5, Scene 2, why does Caithness support Malcolm instead of Macbeth?

....

....

Quote: ....

Q4 Why do you think Shakespeare shows Young Siward's death in Act 5, Scene 7?

....

....

Young Siward's name's more tragic than his death...

In Act 5, Shakespeare uses the Doctor to confirm Lady Macbeth's madness to both the audience and Macbeth. Think about how minor characters are used to reveal key events and move the plot along.

Making Links

A really good way to improve your answers is to make links between your point and different parts of the play. You can do this in lots of different ways, including making links between characters, events or themes. This page will get you thinking about how some of the main characters behave in different parts of the play. Try to only use specific examples — it'll make your points much more convincing.

Q1 Think about how Macbeth and Lady Macbeth change over the course of the play. Give an example from Act 1 which shows what each character is like, then give an example from Act 5 which shows how they have changed.

Character	Act 1	Act 5
Macbeth		
Lady Macbeth		

Q2 Some characters don't change much. For each character below, give a word to describe their personality. Then find two examples from different parts of the play that support each of your descriptions. These could be quotes or examples of things that happen.

Character(s)	Personality	Example One	Example Two
Malcolm			
The Witches			
Banquo			
Macduff			

Practice Questions

Now that you know the characters inside out, it's time to put your knowledge into action. Here are a few practice questions to test what you've learned so far and give you an idea of what it'll be like in the exam. It's important to take your time with this, so tackle each question separately and write a rough plan first.

Q1 Explain how Lady Macbeth is presented as an evil character.
Refer to the extract below and to the play as a whole.

Lady Macbeth:
When you durst do it, then you were a man.
And to be more than what you were, you would
Be so much more the man. Nor time, nor place
Did then adhere, and yet you would make both.
They have made themselves and that their fitness now
Does unmake you. I have given suck and know
How tender 'tis to love the babe that milks me:
I would, while it was smiling in my face,
Have plucked my nipple from his boneless gums
And dashed the brains out, had I so sworn
As you have done to this.

Macbeth:
If we should fail?

Lady Macbeth:
We fail?
But screw your courage to the sticking-place,
And we'll not fail. When Duncan is asleep,
Whereto the rather shall his day's hard journey
Soundly invite him, his two chamberlains
Will I with wine and wassail so convince,
That memory, the warder of the brain,
Shall be a fume, and the receipt of reason
A limbeck only. When in swinish sleep
Their drenchèd natures lie as in a death,
What cannot you and I perform upon
Th'unguarded Duncan?

(Act 1, Scene 7, lines 49-70)

Q2 Read Act 1, Scene 4, lines 33-58. Write about how Duncan is presented in this extract and in the rest of the play.

Q3 Read Act 5, Scene 3, lines 1-23. Explain how Macbeth's state of mind is presented in this extract and in the rest of the play.

Q4 Read Act 5, Scene 8, lines 8-34, then answer the questions below.

a) How is Macbeth presented in this extract?

b) In this extract, Macbeth realises that he has been manipulated by the Witches.
What is the significance of manipulation in the rest of *Macbeth*? Explain your answer.
You should consider:

- times when characters are manipulated
- how this influences their actions.

Ambition

Q1 Explain what each of these quotes shows about Macbeth's attitude to ambition.

a) **"The Prince of Cumberland! That is a step / On which I must fall down, or else o'erleap"** (Act 1, Scene 4, lines 48-49)

....

....

b) **"Upon my head they placed a fruitless crown, / And put a barren sceptre in my gripe"** (Act 3, Scene 1, lines 59-60)

....

....

Q2 Why does Macbeth initially struggle to act on his ambition?

....

....

Q3 Give two ways in which Shakespeare shows that ambition can be a positive force in *Macbeth*.

1) ....

....

2) ....

....

Q4 How does Macbeth's ambition contribute to his downfall?

....

....

Fatal Ambition — the new fragrance by Lady Macbeth...

Read Act 1, Scene 3, lines 118-144. Write an essay plan for this question: **In this extract, Macbeth considers whether to pursue his ambition to be king. In what way is ambition important in the play?** Use the extract and the rest of the play to support your points. You should write about:

- times when ambition influences a character's actions
- how ambition is significant in the play.

Loyalty and Betrayal

Q1 Decide if the following statements are **true** or **false**.

	True	False
Malcolm betrays Duncan in Act 1.	☐	☐
Macbeth is loyal to Duncan at the start of Act 1.	☐	☐
Banquo betrays his own sense of honour.	☐	☐
Macduff is more loyal to his family than his country.	☐	☐
Malcolm is careful about who he trusts.	☐	☐

Q2 In Macbeth's time, subjects were expected to show loyalty to their monarch. How is this reflected in Act 1, Scene 6? Use a quote to support your answer.

....

....

....

Q3 Macbeth and Lady Macbeth both betray Duncan. Why might the audience be less likely to forgive Macbeth for his disloyalty?

....

....

....

Q4 How does Shakespeare suggest that betrayal will always be punished?

....

....

....

....

....

King and Queen Macbeth — the not-so-loyal family...

Think about Macbeth's relationship with Lady Macbeth. Make a few notes about whether you think he shows loyalty to her. You should use examples of events from the play to support your answer.

Kingship

Q1 Fill in the table below to show the characteristics of good kings in *Macbeth*.

Name of King	Characteristic	Quote from play
Malcolm	Just	
Duncan		"worthy Banquo: he is full so valiant, / And in his commendations I am fed" (Act 1, Scene 4, lines 54-55)
Edward	Generous	

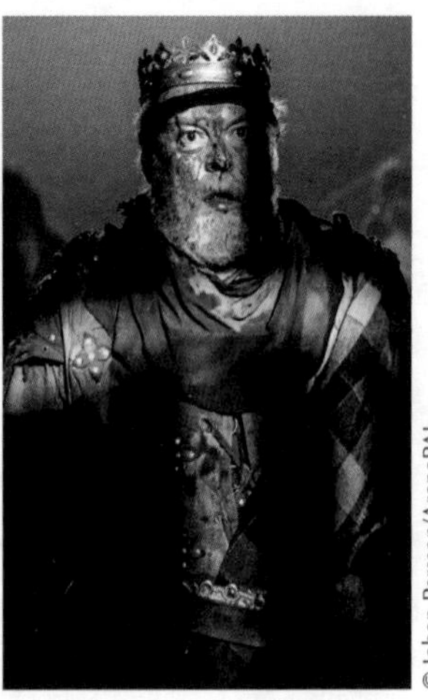

© Johan Persson/ArenaPAL

Q2 In Scotland at the time, the person next in line to the throne didn't necessarily have to be the King's nearest relative. What effect does this have on the events in the play?

....

....

Q3 Macbeth's tyranny becomes more obvious as the play progresses. Find a quote from each of the acts below to show how Macbeth becomes more open about committing evil deeds.

Act 3: ....

....

Act 5: ....

Q4 In Shakespeare's time, many people thought that rightful kings were appointed by God. Using a quote, explain how this is shown in the way Malcolm's kingship is presented.

....

....

....

Macbeth felt right full after his coronation banquet...

Read Act 3, Scene 6, lines 24-50. **Explain how the theme of kingship is presented in *Macbeth*.** You should consider:

- how Shakespeare presents kings in this extract
- how Shakespeare presents kingship in the play as a whole.

Good and Evil

Q1 Why do you think Shakespeare presents Macbeth as an honourable character who gradually becomes an evil tyrant?

....

....

Q2 Read Act 1, Scene 4, lines 44-53 and answer the questions below.

a) How does Shakespeare reveal Macbeth's evil intentions to the audience?

....

b) Find a quote in this extract which shows that Macbeth knows his intentions are evil. What does this suggest about Macbeth's morality at this point?

Quote: ....

Explanation: ....

....

Q3 Read Act 4, Scene 1. How does Shakespeare use stage directions to suggest that the apparitions are a force for evil? Use a quote to support your answer.

....

....

....

Q4 How does Shakespeare use the battle at the end of the play to represent the conflict between good and evil? Back up your answer with examples.

....

....

....

....

The "juggling fiends" were popular in the underworld...

The theme of evil is often linked to gender in *Macbeth*. Write a short paragraph that summarises the different ways that men and women are presented as evil. Include examples to back up your ideas.

The Supernatural

Q1 Find quotes to back up the following statements.

a) The Witches drive the action of the play.

....

b) It's often unclear whether supernatural visions are real or imaginary in the play.

....

c) The supernatural can disrupt the natural world.

....

Q2 Read Act 3, Scene 4, lines 32-116, then answer the questions below. Use quotes to support your answers.

a) How does Shakespeare use the supernatural to create tension in this scene?

....

....

b) How does Shakespeare use Banquo's ghost to highlight Macbeth's guilt?

....

....

Q3 Many people in Shakespeare's time believed that witchcraft was a dangerous force. How is this belief reflected in the play?

....

....

....

....

For breakfast I have organic muesli — it's super natural...

Imagine you're directing a theatre production of *Macbeth*. Jot down a few bullet points on how you would present the Witches to the audience. You should consider:

- what the set (e.g. the scenery and the lighting) would be like when they are on stage
- how the Witches would look and act.

Reality and Appearances

Q1 Why does Macbeth develop a false sense of security as a result of the Witches' prophecies?

....

....

....

Q2 Fill in the table below to give information about attitudes to reality and appearances.

Statement	Quote that shows this
Banquo believes that the truth can be used to give people a false sense of security. (Act 1)	
Macbeth believes that false appearances can hide a person's true nature. (Act 3)	

Q3 How does Shakespeare demonstrate the dangers of trusting in appearances? Support your answer with examples.

....

....

....

....

Q4 Think of a character who is not deceived by Macbeth. Explain how you can tell that they don't trust him. Use an example from the text in your answer.

Name of character: ....

Explanation: ....

....

....

Macbeth had trouble getting his "false face" to stay on...

Jot down three quotes to show that Lady Macbeth finds it increasingly difficult to hide her guilt over her part in Duncan's murder as the play goes on. Each of your quotes should come from a different act.

Fate and Free Will

Q1 Do you think that Macbeth believes in Act 1 that it is his fate to be king? Explain your answer.

....

....

....

....

Q2 What do you think Shakespeare wants the audience to believe about whether fate or free will is more powerful? Explain your answer.

....

....

....

....

© Johan Persson/ArenaPAL

Q3 Find two examples from the text of times when Macbeth seems to be acting out of free will.

1) ....

....

2) ....

....

Q4 At the time the play was written, some people at the time thought that the King (James I) was one of Banquo's descendants. What does this suggest about fate?

....

....

....

....

Free Will — he's trapped inside this book...

If you're asked about fate and free will in the exam, consider whether Shakespeare suggests that the Witches' prophecies were destined to come true, or whether Macbeth's actions made them come true.

Writing about Context

To get a high mark in the exam, you'll need to discuss the context of *Macbeth*. The play was written in the early 17th century, a time of political uncertainty. It's really important that you show the examiner that you understand how context might have influenced Shakespeare when he was writing the play. The exercises on this page will get you to think about the best ways to discuss context.

Q1 Read the sample answer extracts below and underline the contextual information.

a) Throughout the play, the Witches are presented as evil and frightening characters who use their powers to cause harm. In Act 1, Scene 3, Banquo refers to the Witches as the "devil". This comparison with Satan implies that the Witches are evil and faithless. The Witches would have been especially terrifying for 17th-century audiences as witchcraft was believed to be real during this period and many people were frightened of witches.

b) Lady Macbeth's ambition is limited by her gender. When Lady Macbeth is plotting Duncan's murder in Act 1, Scene 5, she asks the spirits to "Come to my woman's breasts / And take my milk for gall". This indicates that Lady Macbeth is willing to sacrifice her femininity and maternal instinct in order to become queen. Lady Macbeth's desire to be more masculine would have shocked a 17th-century audience because at the time women were expected to conform to strictly defined roles as dutiful wives and loving mothers — Lady Macbeth, however, rejects these roles in order to achieve her ambitions.

Q2 The bullet points below form part of a P.E.E.D. paragraph (see p.19). Read through the points and choose an appropriate piece of context from the numbered list which develops the paragraph. Then write a short paragraph explaining your choice.

- Shakespeare uses the events of the play to explore the consequences of bad kingship.
- After the murder of Banquo and the Macduffs, Macbeth is called a "tyrant" by Lennox, Malcolm, Macduff and Young Siward.
- The repetition of the word "tyrant" reinforces to the audience that Macbeth has become an oppressive ruler and that he has lost the respect of those around him.

1) James I had ruled England for approximately three years when *Macbeth* was written.
2) Kings and queens had a lot of power in the early 17th century, so it was extremely important that they ruled well and were respected by the people.
3) The play may have been written in honour of the King, James I, who was Scottish.

Piece of context: ....

Explanation of choice: ....

....

....

....

Practice Questions

Here are a few more delightful exam-style questions to tickle your taste buds. It's important not to rush this — give yourself five minutes or so to plan each answer and make sure you use P.E.E.D. to explain everything clearly. Don't forget to back up all of your points with quotes from the play. You know the drill.

Q1 Explain how the supernatural is presented as powerful in *Macbeth*.
Refer to the extract from Act 2, Scene 1 below and to the play as a whole.

Macbeth: Is this a dagger which I see before me,
The handle toward my hand? Come, let me clutch thee.
I have thee not, and yet I see thee still.
Art thou not, fatal vision, sensible
To feeling as to sight? Or art thou but
A dagger of the mind, a false creation,
Proceeding from the heat-oppressèd brain?
I see thee yet, in form as palpable
As this which now I draw.
Thou marshall'st me the way that I was going,
And such an instrument I was to use.
Mine eyes are made the fools o' the other senses,
Or else worth all the rest. I see thee still,
And on thy blade and dudgeon gouts of blood,
Which was not so before. There's no such thing:
It is the bloody business which informs
Thus to mine eyes. Now o'er the one half-world
Nature seems dead, and wicked dreams abuse
The curtained sleep. Now witchcraft celebrates
Pale Hecate's offerings, and withered murder,
Alarumed by his sentinel, the wolf,
Whose howl's his watch, thus with his stealthy pace,
With Tarquin's ravishing strides, towards his design
Moves like a ghost.

(Act 2, Scene 1, lines 34-57)

Q2 Read Act 3, Scene 5, lines 10-33. How does Shakespeare use the character of Macbeth to explore the theme of fate and free will? Refer to the extract and to the play as a whole.

Q3 Read Act 4, Scene 3, lines 12-37. Write about how the relationship between good and evil is presented in *Macbeth*. Refer to the extract and the rest of the play.

Q4 Read Act 4, Scene 2, lines 1-25, then answer the questions below.

a) How is Lady Macduff presented in this extract?

b) In this extract, it is suggested that Macduff has been disloyal to his family.
What is the significance of disloyalty in *Macbeth*? Explain your answer.
You should consider:
- times when characters are disloyal
- how disloyal behaviour influences other characters.

Form and Structure of 'Macbeth'

Q1 Read the paragraph below and fill in the gaps using the words in the box.

Like most ...., the plot of *Macbeth* is about one main .... and their downfall. Macbeth is introduced to the reader as a .... hero, but his ambition .... him. This ambition is his 'fatal flaw' — the .... in his character that causes his ruin.

weakness
romances
character
heroine
disloyal
tragedies
destroys
noble

Q2 A traitor is beheaded on the battlefield near the start and the end of *Macbeth*. Why does Shakespeare create similarities between the beginning and ending of the play?

....

....

Q3 In Act 1, Scene 1, the audience learns that the Witches are planning to meet with Macbeth. How does this create tension at the start of the play?

....

....

....

Q4 Choose an event that you think is the 'turning point' for Macbeth's fortunes in the play — the event that ultimately causes his downfall. Then explain your choice.

Event: ....

Explanation: ....

....

....

Q5 In Act 1, Scene 3, the Witches curse a sailor on a ship by creating a storm that prevents him from getting any sleep. How does their curse foreshadow Macbeth's experiences later in the play?

....

....

....

Q6 The final act of the play has lots of short scenes. Explain how this affects the pace of the plot.

Q7 The idea of murdering Duncan occurs to Macbeth in Act 1, Scene 3, but the murder doesn't take place until after Act 2, Scene 1. What effect does this have on the audience?

Q8 Shakespeare creates suspense by making the audience question what may happen later in the play. Write down what question is raised by each of these events. The first one has been done for you.

Event	What question is raised?
a) Act 2, Scene 3: Malcolm and Donalbain feel threatened following Duncan's murder.	Will they be murdered later in the play?
b) Act 3, Scene 4: Macbeth acts strangely in front of the thanes when he sees Banquo's ghost.	
c) Act 4, Scene 1: The Witches tell Macbeth to "**beware Macduff**".	

Q9 Read Macbeth's speech in Act 3, Scene 2, lines 45-56 and Lady Macbeth's soliloquy in Act 1, Scene 5, lines 39-53.

A soliloquy is a speech in which a character thinks out loud about their emotions. It's not directed at any other characters.

a) Write down one similarity between these passages.

b) Why do you think Shakespeare wants the audience to compare Macbeth with Lady Macbeth at this point in the play?

You get the idea Macbeth should've scene it coming...

The fact that *Macbeth* is a tragedy links to the theme of good and evil. Macbeth's character is shown to have lots of noble qualities, but his 'fatal flaw' (ambition) leads him to commit evil acts.

Mood and Atmosphere

Q1 What type of mood is created by the setting in the first scene of the play? Explain your answer.

....

....

....

Q2 How does the dialogue between the Porter and Macduff in Act 2, Scene 3 create a light-hearted mood?

....

....

....

Q3 Explain what atmosphere is created by each of the quotes below.

a) "**But now I am cabined, cribbed, confined, bound in / To saucy doubts and fears.**" (Act 3, Scene 4, lines 24-25)

....

....

b) "**Thy bones are marrowless, thy blood is cold; / Thou hast no speculation in those eyes**" (Act 3, Scene 4, lines 94-95)

....

....

Q4 Why do you think the final scene of the play begins and ends with a "***Flourish***" (the playing of a fanfare)?

....

....

....

Guilt and despair — this play was destined for exams...

Make a list of four scenes from *Macbeth* that bring about a change in the play's mood. Then write a couple of sentences next to each of the scenes you've chosen, explaining how the mood changes.

Poetry in Shakespeare

Blank verse is a type of poetry. Its lines have 10 or 11 syllables, 5 main beats and they don't usually rhyme.

Q1 Find one quote from the play that is written in:

a) Unrhymed blank verse ....

....

b) Rhyme ....

....

Q2 Why do you think Shakespeare makes the Witches speak in rhyme? Give two reasons.

1) ....

2) ....

Q3 Read Act 2, Scene 3, lines 80-112, then answer the questions below.

a) Find a sentence in this passage that contains several long words.

....

....

....

b) Explain why you think Shakespeare includes longer words at this point in the passage.

....

....

Q4 Read Act 5, Scene 1, lines 31-34. Explain what rhythm is created in this passage, then say what this rhythm suggests about Lady Macbeth's emotions at this point in the play.

....

....

....

A poet AND a playwright? — Show off...

Find a soliloquy in *Macbeth*, then write a short paragraph explaining what the soliloquy you've chosen reveals about the character who performs it. Make sure you include a quote in your answer.

Puns and Wordplay

Q1 Read the paragraph below and fill in the gaps using the words in the box.

A pun is sometimes formed when a word has more than one ....

Puns are often ...., so Shakespeare uses them to ....

the audience. He also uses them to reveal .... thoughts and feelings.

shock	characters'	emotional	entertain	his	calm	funny	sad	insult	meaning

Q2 In Act 1, Scene 5, Lady Macbeth tells Macbeth to "**put / This night's great business into my dispatch**" (lines 66-67). In this sentence, "**into my dispatch**" means 'into my care', but "**dispatch**" can also mean 'to kill'. What is the effect of this pun? Explain your answer.

....

....

....

Q3 Read Act 2, Scene 3, line 48.

a) Write down the word that creates wordplay in this line.

....

b) How does this wordplay create dramatic irony?

Dramatic irony is when the audience knows something that the characters on stage don't know.

....

....

....

Q4 The Witches often use paradoxes (contradictory phrases). How does this wordplay affect the audience's opinion of them?

....

....

....

The exam is about as unpunny as this joke here...

Boy, Shakespeare sure loved his puns and wordplay. It's a good idea to have three or four examples up your sleeve for the exam — it'll give you a chance to show the examiner some language analysis.

Imagery and Symbolism

Q1 Fill in the gaps in table below. Some have been done for you.

Type of imagery	Quote	Effect
Simile	"**they were / As cannons overcharged with double cracks**" (Act 1, Scene 2, lines 36-37)	Comparing Macbeth and Banquo to heavily loaded cannons makes their actions on the battlefield seem powerful and heroic.
Metaphor		
	"**Our castle's strength / Will laugh a siege to scorn**" (Act 5, Scene 5, lines 2-3)	

Q2 'Light is a symbol of goodness in the play.' Find a quote that backs up this statement, then explain its meaning.

Quote: ....

Meaning: ....

....

Q3 How does Shakespeare link darkness with evil? Use quotes to support your answer.

....

....

....

....

Q4 Find three pieces of imagery which suggest that nature is disrupted by Duncan's murder.

1) ....

2) ....

3) ....

Q5 How is imagery of sickness and injury used to present Macbeth's rule in a negative way?

Q6 Read the following statements about symbolism and imagery in *Macbeth*, then decide whether they are **true** or **false**.

	True	False
Religious imagery is used to emphasise the difference between good and evil.	☐	☐
Light being extinguished is used to symbolise Banquo's death.	☐	☐
Thunder is used to symbolise Lady Macbeth's evil acts.	☐	☐
Duncan's dialogue contains plant imagery.	☐	☐

Q7 How is blood linked to Lady Macbeth's guilty conscience? Use a quote in your answer.

Q8 Give an example from the play that links masculinity to:

a) Violence

b) Sensitivity

Q9 What do you think sleeplessness symbolises in the play? Give a reason for your answer.

I metaphor once — he had a neighbour called phive...

Read Act 3, Scene 2, lines 35-56. **How is Macbeth presented as evil in this extract and in the rest of the play?** Write an answer to this question, making sure to include an introduction and a conclusion.

Working with Extracts

In the exam, there will be a question that asks you to write about an extract. Examiners love extract questions as they demonstrate your ability to discuss a short passage in detail. They're also a great opportunity for you to really focus on language analysis, showing that you understand how language creates meaning. This page will help you to develop the skills needed to ace any extract question.

COURTYARD IN MACBETH'S CASTLE

Enter LADY MACBETH

Lady Macbeth: That which hath made them drunk hath made me bold;
What hath quenched them hath given me fire. Hark! Peace!
It was the owl that shrieked, the fatal bellman,
Which gives the stern'st good-night. He is about it.
The doors are open, and the surfeited grooms
Do mock their charge with snores — I have drugged their possets,
That death and nature do contend about them,
Whether they live or die.

Macbeth: (Within) Who's there? What, ho!

Lady Macbeth: Alack, I am afraid they have awaked,
And 'tis not done. The attempt and not the deed
Confounds us. Hark! I laid their daggers ready;
He could not miss 'em. Had he not resembled
My father as he slept, I had done't.

(Act 2, Scene 2, lines 1-13)

Q1 Read through the extract above. Describe what has just happened in the play before this extract and what is about to happen after it.

....

....

Q2 Underline an example of a metaphor in the extract.

Q3 In this extract, Lady Macbeth uses short sentences. What effect does this have?

....

....

Q4 Lady Macbeth claims she would have killed Duncan if he hadn't looked like her father. Find a second example of when Lady Macbeth shows vulnerability in the play.

....

....

Practice Questions

Now you've got to grips with all those techniques, it's time to have a stab at some practice exam questions. If you're struggling, look back at your answers for this section — they might give you some inspiration.

Q1 How does Shakespeare create tension in *Macbeth*? You must refer to the extract below and the play as a whole in your answer.

THE ENTRANCE TO MACBETH'S CASTLE

Enter a PORTER. *Knocking within.*

Porter: Here's a knocking indeed — if a man were porter of hell-gate, he should have old turning the key.

(*Knock*)

Knock, knock, knock. Who's there i'th'name of Beelzebub? Here's a farmer that hanged himself on th'expectation of plenty. Come in time — have napkins enough about you, here you'll sweat for't.

(*Knock*)

Knock, knock. Who's there in th'other devil's name? Faith, here's an equivocator that could swear in both the scales against either scale, who committed treason enough for God's sake, yet could not equivocate to heaven. O, come in, equivocator.

(*Knock*)

Knock, knock, knock. Who's there? Faith, here's an English tailor come hither for stealing out of a French hose. Come in, tailor, here you may roast your goose.

(*Knock*)

Knock, knock. Never at quiet! What are you? But this place is too cold for hell. I'll devil-porter it no further — I had thought to have let in some of all professions that go the primrose way to th'everlasting bonfire.

(Act 2, Scene 3, lines 1-18)

Q2 Read Act 4, Scene 1, lines 12-34. Write about how Shakespeare creates a sinister atmosphere in *Macbeth*. You should discuss the extract and the play as a whole.

Q3 Read Act 1, Scene 7, lines 28-47.

a) Explain how conflict between Macbeth and Lady Macbeth is presented in this extract.

b) In this extract, Lady Macbeth discusses Macbeth's ambition to be king. Explain how ambition is presented in other parts of the play. You should consider:

- where ambition appears
- how it affects characters in the play.

Q4 Read Act 4, Scene 3, lines 159-173.
How is Scotland presented as troubled in this extract and in the play as a whole?

Understanding the Question

Underline key words in the question

Q1 Underline the most important words in the following questions. The first one has been done for you.

a) Write about the importance of the supernatural in *Macbeth*.

b) To what extent is Macbeth presented as a strong character in the play?

c) Explore how the relationship between Macbeth and Lady Macbeth is presented.

d) How does Shakespeare use the Witches to explore the theme of reality and appearances?

e) Explain how Shakespeare presents Banquo in the play.

f) How is the theme of fate and free will presented in the play?

g) Write about the significance of Duncan in the play.

Make sure you understand exam language

Q2 Match each exam question to the correct explanation of what you would need to do to answer it. You'll only need to use each white box once.

a) To what extent is Macbeth presented as a strong character in the play?

b) Write about the importance of the supernatural in *Macbeth*.

c) Write about the significance of Duncan in the play.

d) How is the theme of fate and free will in the play?

e) Explore how the relationship between Macbeth and Lady Macbeth is presented.

1) Analyse how a theme contributes to the action of the play.

2) Analyse how far a judgement or description is correct.

3) Analyse how Shakespeare writes about a theme in the play.

4) Analyse how a character contributes to the action and overall message of the play.

5) Analyse how characters interact and impact on each other.

Don't panic in the exam — take a deep Macbreath...

When you're told to start your exam, it's hard not to just dive in and write as much as you can. But this won't help you get a good grade — firstly, read the question several times and consider what it's really asking you.

Making a Rough Plan

Jot down your main ideas

Q1 Look at the exam question below, then complete the spider diagram with at least three more main points for answering it.

Don't forget to underline the key words in the question before you start.

Macbeth uses poetic language to hide his involvement in Duncan's murder.

Read Act 2, Scene 3 from line 100 to line 118.
How is the theme of reality and appearances presented in *Macbeth*?
Use the extract and the play as a whole in your answer.

Put your main points and examples in a logical order

Q2 Choose your three main points from Q1 and fill in the plan below, adding evidence (a quote or an example from the text) for each point.

One or two of your points should be about the extract from Q1.

(Introduction)

Point One: ....

Evidence: ....

Point Two: ....

Evidence: ....

Point Three: ....

Evidence: ....

(Conclusion)

Is this a spider diagram which I see before me?

In the exam, it's really important that you make a plan before you start writing each answer. Plans help you to stay focused and help you to stick to the most relevant points. And they should only take around 5 minutes...

Making Links

Make links with other parts of the text

Q1 Look at the exam question and the table below. Complete the table with other relevant parts of the text which could be used to back up each point.

Explore how the relationship between Macbeth and Lady Macbeth is presented.

Point	Example 1	Example 2
Lady Macbeth has power over her husband.	Lady Macbeth questions Macbeth's masculinity.	
Macbeth loves and admires his wife.	Macbeth suggests that Lady Macbeth is his partner.	
Macbeth isn't very caring towards Lady Macbeth.	Macbeth goes off to fight instead of helping Lady Macbeth when she is ill.	

Extend your essay with other examples

You won't have time to do really detailed planning in the exam, so you should get into the habit of thinking of links when you're doing practice questions.

Q2 Take each of your points from the plan you made in Q2 on p.51, and write down another example from elsewhere in the text that you could include in your essay.

Example for Point One: ....

....

Example for Point Two: ....

....

Example for Point Three: ....

....

"Macbeth shall sleep no more" — must be exam week...

To show the examiner you have a solid understanding of the play, you have to be able to make links — this makes your answers more persuasive. Try noting down any links that you come across while reading the text.

Structuring Your Answer

P.E.E.D. stands for Point, Example, Explain, Develop

Q1 Read the following extract from an exam answer. Label each aspect of P.E.E.D.

> Macbeth is troubled by his conscience. For example, in Act 1, Scene 7, Macbeth voices his fears about "deep damnation" after death. This suggests that he is aware of the consequences of his actions and knows that he will suffer as a result of killing the King. There is a strong contrast in this scene between Macbeth and Lady Macbeth, who shows no concern or guilt for her actions.

Embedding quotes is a great way to give evidence

Q2 Rewrite the following sentences so that a short part of the quote is embedded in each one.

a) The Witches call Macbeth evil. — "Something wicked this way comes."

....

b) Duncan is considered to be a good king. — "The gracious Duncan / Was pitied of Macbeth"

....

Structure your answer using the P.E.E.D. method

Q3 Use the P.E.E.D. method to structure a paragraph on your first point from Q2 on page 51.

Point: ....

....

Example: ....

....

Explain: ....

....

Develop: ....

....

[Insert obvious joke here]...

You should always use the P.E.E.D. structure in your exam as it helps to make your answers brilliantly clear and concise. A good way to remember the structure is to come up with a funny joke about it — the ruder the better.

Introductions and Conclusions

Give a clear answer to the question in your introduction

Q1 Read the introductions below, then decide which is better. Explain your choice.

To what extent is Lady Macbeth presented as an ambitious character in *Macbeth*?

a) Throughout the play, Lady Macbeth is presented by Shakespeare as an extremely ambitious character. She demonstrates this ambition through her willingness to forsake her femininity and to manipulate other characters, in order to become queen. Her death, however, shows the limitations of her ambition because her life is taken over by her guilt.

b) Ambition is an important theme in the play, and both Macbeth and Lady Macbeth are presented as very ambitious. For example, Lady Macbeth is an extremely ambitious character whose evil nature encourages her to convince her husband to kill the King. Macbeth is also presented as an ambitious character — he murders several people in order to seize and maintain power.

Better intro: .... Reason: ....

....

....

....

Don't write any new points in your conclusion

Q2 Read this conclusion to the exam question in Q1, then say how it could be improved.

In conclusion, Lady Macbeth is presented as a ruthless character throughout the play. However, her ambition becomes the cause of her eventual downfall. As well as this point, she belittles Macbeth because he is too scared to follow his ambition, which suggests that she thinks she is superior to him.

....

....

....

....

....

My conclusion? This play's about as bloody as it gets...

Write an introduction and conclusion for the exam question on page 51. Keep in mind the good and bad examples on this page and make sure you always make the introduction and conclusion relevant to the question.

Writing about Context

Make sure you can link the play to its context

Q1 Match each statement with the relevant contextual information.

a) Lady Macbeth has a lot of influence over her husband and questions his masculinity.

b) The Witches play a key role in the play — they manipulate Macbeth into believing he will be king.

c) The Witches claim that Banquo's descendants will be the future kings of Scotland.

1) Women in the 17th century were expected to obey their husbands.

2) James I, who was King when *Macbeth* was written, was believed to be a descendant of the real Banquo.

3) Many people in Shakespearean England believed in witchcraft.

Include context in your answer

Q2 Read the sample answer extract below and underline the contextual information.

Throughout the play, many characters use false appearances to mask evil thoughts. For example, Lady Macbeth encourages Macbeth to "look like th'innocent flower, / But be the serpent under't" when Duncan comes to their castle. Here, Lady Macbeth uses a simile to suggest that Macbeth should act in an "innocent" manner to mask his treachery. 17th-century England was very religious so the image of the "serpent" would have made audiences at the time think of Satan taking the form of a snake in the Bible. This would have made Lady Macbeth seem even more evil.

Q3 Now write a paragraph on either your second or third point from page 51.
You should include contextual information and use the P.E.E.D. method.

....

....

....

....

....

....

Include some context or the examiner will be con-vexed...

In the exam, you need to show the examiner that you understand the relationship between the play and its context. There are loads of ways you can do this, just make sure your context is always relevant to the point you're making.

Linking Ideas and Paragraphs

Link your ideas so your argument is easy to follow

Q1 Rewrite the sample answer below so that the ideas are clearly linked.

> Throughout the play, Macbeth is plagued by visions. In Act 2, Scene 1, Macbeth asks, "is this a dagger which I see before me...?" Macbeth has begun his descent into madness as he can no longer trust his own judgement. Lady Macbeth is presented as mad when she begins to hallucinate a "damned spot" of blood.

Q2 Write a paragraph using your remaining point from p.51. Make sure your ideas are properly linked.

Show how your paragraphs follow on from each other

Q3 Look at the paragraphs you have written on p.53, p.55 and on this page using your points from p.51. Write down linking words or phrases you could use to link them together in your answer.

Paragraphs to link	Linking word or phrase
Points 1 and 2	
Points 2 and 3	

Paragraphs should be like daggers — short and to the point...

Read the question carefully and make a plan before you write your answer. If you know what you want to say before you start writing, the links between your ideas will be a lot clearer. And remember to use P.E.E.D.

Marking Answer Extracts

Get familiar with the mark scheme

Grade band	An answer at this level...
8-9	• shows an insightful and critical personal response to the text • closely and perceptively analyses how the writer uses language, form and structure to create meaning and affect the reader, making use of highly relevant subject terminology • supports arguments with well-integrated, highly relevant and precise examples from the text • gives a detailed exploration of the relationship between the text and its context • uses highly varied vocabulary and sentence types, with mostly accurate spelling and punctuation
6-7	• shows a critical and observant personal response to the text • includes a thorough exploration of how the writer uses language, form and structure to create meaning and affect the reader, making use of appropriate subject terminology • supports arguments with integrated, well-chosen examples from the text • explores the relationship between the text and its context • uses a substantial range of vocabulary and sentence types, with generally accurate spelling and punctuation
4-5	• shows a thoughtful and clear personal response to the text • examines how the writer uses language, form and structure to create meaning and affect the reader, making some use of relevant subject terminology • integrates appropriate examples from the text • shows an understanding of contextual factors • uses a moderate range of vocabulary and sentence types, without spelling and punctuation errors which make the meaning unclear

Have a go at marking an answer extract

Q1 Using the mark scheme, put the sample answer extract below in a grade band and explain why.

How is Banquo presented as a good character in *Macbeth*?

Shakespeare shows that Banquo is a good character in the play. He does this through other characters' positive opinions of him. For example, Lennox calls him "right-valiant Banquo". This shows that he is good. Lenox's character is a Scottish noble, which was an important position in Shakespeare's day. The audiance would view Banquo as a good character in contrast to Macbeth, whose behaviour gets worse as the play goes on.

Grade band: .... Reason: ....

....

....

....

Marking Answer Extracts

Have a look at these extracts from answers to the question on p.57

Q1 For each extract, say what grade band you think it is in, then underline an example of where it meets each of the mark scheme criteria. Label each underlined point to show what it achieves.

a) Shakespeare emphasises Banquo's virtue by encouraging the audience to directly compare him with Macbeth, who is shown to be an evil character. The characters are first introduced when the Captain describes how they "Doubly redoubled strokes upon the foe" in battle. The repeated idea of 'double' and the fact that their actions are described together emphasise Banquo and Macbeth's partnership. By showing how they were once so similar, Shakespeare emphasises the differences that later emerge between them; Macbeth's moral degeneration highlights Banquo's virtue to the audience. This comparison is reinforced in Act 2 when Banquo's virtuous nature means that he chooses to keep his "allegiance clear" rather than supporting Macbeth, who he considers morally questionable.

Unlike Macbeth, Banquo is able to control his ambition, which demonstrates that he is a good character. Although he dwells on the Witches' prophecies, he resists pursuing them. This is highlighted in Act 3, Scene 1, when he says "But hush! No more" to stifle his ambitious thoughts. These short sentences make the line sound fragmented, reflecting Banquo's interrupted thoughts and emphasising his determination to suppress his ambition. His resolve implies that his actions are still governed by his morality. Banquo's effort to distance himself from the Witches would have given a particularly strong indication of his virtue to 17th-century audience members; many would have believed in the devil and its association with witchcraft in a way that modern audience members might not.

Grade band: ....

b) Shakespeare shows that Banquo is an honourable character throughout the play. In Act 3, Scene 1, just after Banquo has left Macbeth's castle with Fleance, Macbeth reveals that he fears Banquo's "royalty of nature". By describing Banquo's nature as royal, Macbeth suggests that his personality has an honourable quality, as 17th-century audience members would have associated royalty with good morals. Banquo's strong principles are emphasised just before his death through his cry of "O, treachery!" Even though he is suspicious of Macbeth, Banquo is surprised to find himself in danger because his own morals lead him to assume that Macbeth will not behave dishonourably towards him.

Banquo is also presented as a loyal character in the play. When he learns of Duncan's murder in Act 2, Scene 3, he says "Against the undivulged pretence I fight / Of treasonous malice". The word "treasonous" suggests that Banquo sees the murder as a betrayal of Duncan, who should have been shown loyalty as a monarch of Scotland. The idea that Duncan was owed loyalty is reinforced through the way Shakespeare presents him as a good king. He rewards Macbeth and Banquo well for their efforts in battle and is referred to after his death as "a most sainted king" by Macduff, suggesting that he was a rightful ruler. This implies that Banquo was right to be loyal to Duncan and emphasises the idea that his loyalty makes him a good character.

Grade band: ....

Marking a Whole Answer

Now try marking this whole answer

Q1 Read the sample answer below. On page 60, put it in a grade band and explain your decision.

> Read Act 1, Scene 5, line 53 to line 72. Explain why the relationship between Macbeth and Lady Macbeth is important to the play.
> You should write about the extract and the play as a whole in your answer.

If it helps you, label examples of where the answer meets the mark scheme criteria.

In *Macbeth*, Shakespeare uses the relationship between Macbeth and Lady Macbeth to explore some of the central themes of the play. The way their relationship changes stresses the powerful and dangerous nature of ambition and encourages the audience to think about the role of the supernatural. Their relationship also reveals important aspects of their characters. Lady Macbeth's eventual isolation from Macbeth shows her vulnerability, which contrasts with her forceful role in their relationship at the start of the play. The growing distance in their relationship highlights Macbeth's preoccupation with the Witches' prophecies and emphasises the 'fatal flaw' that leads to his downfall.

Shakespeare uses the relationship between Macbeth and Lady Macbeth to reflect the strength of their ambition. Macbeth and Lady Macbeth's relationship is at its strongest in the first act of the play. In the extract, their dialogue often combines to form one line of blank verse. For example, Macbeth's line, "We will speak further —" is completed by Lady Macbeth when she says, "Only look up clear". The way they finish one another's lines when plotting to kill Duncan emphasises their partnership to the audience and suggests that their joint ambition for Macbeth to become king unites them. This idea is supported by the distance that develops in their relationship later in the play. When Lady Macbeth's ambition grows weak and is replaced by remorse, she and Macbeth grow further apart.

The relationship between Macbeth and Lady Macbeth also highlights Lady Macbeth's controlling nature. In this extract, which comes from the first scene in which Lady Macbeth and Macbeth appear together in the play, Shakespeare establishes Lady Macbeth's control over Macbeth. She uses imperatives like "be" and "look like" to give orders to her husband, and it is she, not Macbeth, who vocalises the plan to "dispatch" Duncan. Lady Macbeth is therefore presented straight away as the authority in their relationship. Her controlling character would have shocked a 17th-century audience, as they would have expected a wife to submit to her husband's will. By giving Lady Macbeth different values from those of a typical 17th-century woman, Shakespeare encourages the audience to consider their own ideas about femininity.

However, the way Lady Macbeth tries to control Macbeth in the play also exposes her vulnerability as a woman. In the extract, she gives detailed instructions to Macbeth, advising him on how to arrange his "face", "eye", "hand" and "tongue" in order to deceive others. Her focus on controlling Macbeth's different body parts makes him seem like her puppet, which highlights her own powerlessness and her need to act through him. Although her mind has a 'man's' violent and ambitious thoughts, she is restricted in her actions by her woman's body. This restriction is emphasised throughout the play by the fact that, in contrast to Macbeth, who appears alongside several other characters, the only onstage relationship Lady Macbeth has is with her husband. As her world in the play is so limited, the weakening of her relationship with Macbeth leaves her completely isolated and vulnerable.

The increasing isolation in the relationship between Macbeth and Lady Macbeth highlights Macbeth's growing preoccupation with the supernatural in the play. Although in Act 1 Macbeth is "rapt" after encountering the Witches, he only decides to murder Duncan under pressure from Lady Macbeth. However, after Macbeth sees Banquo's ghost in Act 3, Scene 4, he tells his wife he wishes to consult the Witches, stating he is "bent to know" the

This answer continues on p.60. ⟶

Marking a Whole Answer

worst that will happen. The word "bent" shows the powerful hold that the supernatural has over Macbeth, as it suggests he is unable to resist the pull of the Witches' prophetic powers and highlights the way that his decisions are increasingly swayed by the Witches. This shift in the role of the supernatural is also reflected in the structure of the play. After Act 3, Scene 4, Lady Macbeth only appears on stage once more and without Macbeth, while the Witches' stage presence increases in comparison. They appear alone in Act 3, Scene 5 and feature alongside Macbeth in a particularly long scene at the start of Act 4.

The unravelling of Macbeth and Lady Macbeth's relationship reveals the destructive nature of ambition in the play. Lady Macbeth is driven mad with remorse for their actions and Macbeth inadvertently accelerates his own death through his violent attempts to consolidate power. Both of their deaths come as a result of their ambition, which suggests that when ambition isn't restrained by morals, it can be dangerous. Through the couple's downfall, Shakespeare suggests that their reckless and violent acts are futile; neither Macbeth nor Lady Macbeth feels secure following Duncan's murder. An early 17th-century audience would have been well aware of the precarious position the murder puts them in, having just witnessed the consequences of a failed real-life attempt to overthrow the King (James I).

Shakespeare also uses Macbeth and Lady Macbeth's relationship to highlight important elements of the play's tragic form. Macbeth and Lady Macbeth are driven apart by Macbeth's ambition for power, which is his 'fatal flaw': the weakness in a tragic hero's character that causes his downfall. As Macbeth becomes more independent from Lady Macbeth, he also becomes more reckless. After Banquo's murder, he comments that his ambitious thoughts "must be acted ere they may be scanned". This impulsive attitude proves to be his undoing, as the murder of Macduff's family motivates Macduff to pursue Macbeth and kill him. Shakespeare foreshadows this downfall in Act 4 when Hecate states that "security / Is mortals' chiefest enemy". Here, Hecate indicates that Macbeth's overconfidence, which leads him to act without Lady Macbeth's input, endangers him and contributes to his downfall.

In conclusion, it is clear that the relationship between Macbeth and Lady Macbeth contributes to the audience's opinion of their individual characters. Some of these opinions may have been felt more strongly by a 17th-century audience, who lived in society that had more fixed gender roles. In addition, the relationship between Macbeth and Lady Macbeth also develops important themes in the play. Not only does it help to reveal important aspects of ambition, but it also highlights the power of the supernatural.

Grade band: .... Reasons: ....

....

....

....

....

....

Poor Mark — he's always being judged...

Knowing what you need to do to get a good mark in the exam is really important. If you practise including things like language analysis, structure and context now, it'll be second nature by the time you do the exam.

Writing Well

It might seem obvious, but it's important that you use the correct spelling, punctuation and grammar (SPaG for short) in your exam. 5% of the marks in your English Literature GCSE are for writing well, which includes using a wide range of vocabulary, technical terms and sentence structures, as well as accurate SPaG. It's best if you leave yourself a few minutes at the end of the exam to check over your work and correct any mistakes. If you see one, draw a line through it and put your correction above.

Q1 Read the sample answer below. Underline all of the SPaG mistakes, then correct them. One has already been done for you.

> Thane
>
> When Macbeth is made Thain of Cawdor, he realises that the Whiches' first prediction has come true. This gives him more confidense in the prophecy that he will be king. He writes a letter about the Witches' predictions to lady macbeth, who begins to devise a plot to kill Duncan and become queen. The urgency of her planing hints at her evil nature.

Q2 Match each technical term to the correct example. You'll only need to use each example once.

a) Metaphor	**1)** "like a giant's robe / Upon a dwarfish thief."
b) Simile	**2)** "There's daggers in men's smiles"
c) Rhyming couplets	**3)** "fill me from the crown to the toe topfull / Of direst cruelty"
d) Pathetic fallacy	**4)** "Fair is foul, and foul is fair, / Hover through the fog and filthy air."
e) Pun	**5)** *"Thunder and lightning"*
f) Personification	**6)** "the air / Nimbly and sweetly recommends itself"

Practice Questions

Now you've got the skills to impress the examiner, it's time to try them out on this final set of practice questions. This time, try to answer each one under exam conditions — give yourself 5 minutes to write a quick plan then spend about 40 minutes on the answer. Use what you've just learnt and you'll be brilliant.

Q1 To what extent does Shakespeare present Macbeth's mind as weak? Refer to the extract from Act 3, Scene 4 below and to the play as a whole.

Macbeth: Both sides are even; here I'll sit i'th'midst.
Be large in mirth, anon we'll drink a measure
The table round.
(*To First Murderer*) There's blood upon thy face.

First Murderer: 'Tis Banquo's then.

Macbeth: 'Tis better thee without, than he within.
Is he dispatched?

First Murderer: My lord, his throat is cut; that I did for him.

Macbeth: Thou art the best o'th'cut-throats,
Yet he's good that did the like for Fleance;
If thou didst it, thou art the nonpareil.

First Murderer: Most royal sir, Fleance is scaped.

Macbeth: Then comes my fit again — I had else been perfect;
Whole as the marble, founded as the rock,
As broad and general as the casing air.
But now I am cabined, cribbed, confined, bound in
To saucy doubts and fears. But Banquo's safe?

First Murderer: Ay, my good lord, safe in a ditch he bides,
With twenty trenched gashes on his head,
The least a death to nature.

Macbeth: Thanks for that.
There the grown serpent lies; the worm that's fled
Hath nature that in time will venom breed,
No teeth for th'present.

(Act 3, Scene 4, lines 10-31)

Q2 **a)** Read Act 1, Scene 7, lines 1-29. How might the audience react to Macbeth's inner thoughts in this extract?

b) Discuss times in the play when Lady Macbeth may deserve sympathy.

Q3 Read Act 4, Scene 3, lines 111-137. How does Shakespeare present the significance of misplaced trust in the play? Refer to the extract and the play as a whole.

Q4 Read Act 2, Scene 2, lines 30-57, then answer the questions below.

a) Explain how Lady Macbeth's control over Macbeth is presented in this extract.

b) Macbeth's conscience is troubled by his evil deeds in this extract. What is the significance of evil in *Macbeth*? Explain your answer. You should consider:

- times when characters commit evil acts
- how this affects them.

Answers

Section One — Analysis of Acts

Page 2: Act One — Scenes 1 and 2

1. E.g. It creates suspense for the audience.
2. That nothing is really what it seems.
3. E.g. It suggests that they have an important role to play and may influence the rest of the action.
4. The Captain fought to protect Malcolm during the battle.
5. E.g. The way Macbeth "unseamed" his enemy "from the nave to the chops" makes him seem like a strong and ruthless warrior.
6. a) E.g. "O valiant cousin! Worthy gentleman!" (line 24)
   b) E.g. "But I am faint, my gashes cry for help." (line 42)

Page 3: Act One — Scene 3

1. They send a storm to disturb his sleep.
2. They remind the audience of the last lines of the first scene, where the Witches suggest that nothing is what it seems. This hints that Macbeth isn't what he seems to be either.
3. The statements should be numbered 4, 1, 5, 2, 3.
4. E.g. Macbeth: isn't sure whether to believe them at first and wants the Witches to give him more information.
   E.g. Banquo: is suspicious of the Witches' motives but is intrigued to know more about his future.
5. a) He starts to trust the prophecies more, as he knows that two of them have come true.
   b) He becomes obsessed by the thought of becoming king, and can't stop thinking about his future.

Page 4: Act One — Scenes 4 and 5

1. Cawdor, Malcolm, defeat, ambition
2. E.g. "I have begun to plant thee, and will labour / To make thee full of growing." (lines 28-29) This metaphor of plants suggests that Duncan wants to nurture Macbeth.
3. E.g. She seems ruthless because she plans to kill Duncan so that Macbeth can become king. She also seems manipulative when she persuades Macbeth that Duncan must be killed.
4. a) Macbeth is too kind to kill Duncan.
   b) Macbeth needs to appear innocent in front of Duncan even though he is actually plotting to kill him.

Page 5: Act One — Scenes 6 and 7

1. Duncan speaks positively about the castle, commenting that it has a "pleasant seat". He seems pleased to see Lady Macbeth and calls her "our honoured hostess!"
2. a) True: e.g. "we but teach / Bloody instructions, which being taught, return / To plague th'inventor" (lines 8-10).
   b) True: "Who should against his murderer shut the door, / Not bear the knife myself" (lines 15-16).
   c) False: "I have no spur / To prick the sides of my intent, but only / Vaulting ambition" (lines 25-27).
3. She uses persuasive language and questions Macbeth's courage and masculinity. She also makes the murder seem simple by coming up with a clear plan.

Task: You should have written your entry from Macbeth's point of view. Here are some points you may have included:

- Macbeth fights on the battlefield, killing the treacherous Macdonald. He feels honoured by the praise that Duncan gives him for this feat, which later contributes to his initial feeling that killing Duncan would be wrong.
- He meets the Witches and hears their prophecies. He feels horrified by the dark thoughts he has about killing Duncan to fulfil the prophecies, which briefly stops him from pursuing the idea further.
- Macbeth becomes the new Thane of Cawdor, fulfilling the Witches' first prophecy. This makes Macbeth hopeful that the other prophecy could come true, causing him to reconsider the idea of betraying Duncan.
- He allows himself to be influenced by Lady Macbeth, as he feels humiliated when she questions his masculinity. He believes they can work together to achieve greatness, leading him to decide that killing Duncan is a good idea.

Page 6: Act Two — Scenes 1 and 2

1. He uses images of darkness, which are linked to the theme of evil. For instance, the "moon is down" and Banquo says that the stars aren't shining: "Their candles are all out."
2. Initially, Macbeth isn't sure whether the dagger is real or not. He gradually becomes more convinced by its insistence that he go to Duncan's room, which suggests that he has overcome his unease and is ready to kill Duncan.
3. Macbeth: e.g. "How is't with me, when every noise appals me?" (line 58)
   Lady Macbeth: e.g. "Alack, I am afraid they have awaked" (line 9).
4. She seems anxious at the start of the scene, but later takes control, ordering Macbeth to leave the daggers by Duncan's body and smear his servants with blood. When Macbeth says he's too afraid, she goes to do this herself.
5. Macbeth's feeling of guilt is clear when he asks whether "great Neptune's ocean" will "wash this blood / Clean" from his hand. This image of water washing away blood shows his desire to wash away his guilt.

Page 7: Act Two — Scenes 3 and 4

1. The statements should be numbered 3, 4, 2, 5, 6, 1.
2. E.g. She could have actually fainted if she was in shock over Macbeth killing the servants. **Or** e.g. she might be pretending in order to distract the other characters from Macbeth's suspicious behaviour.
3. Running away from the murder scene makes them look guilty, so Macbeth is able to blame them for the murder.
4. E.g. Horses have been eating each other. Events like this suggest that Macbeth's actions have disturbed the natural order.
5. E.g. Macduff doesn't go to Macbeth's coronation.

Task: You should have written your letter from Malcolm's perspective. Here are some points you may have included:

- While staying at Macbeth's castle, Malcolm is told by Macbeth and Macduff that his father, King Duncan, has been murdered.
- He decides to flee to England, where he'll be safe.
- Malcolm suspects that Macbeth's grief is false.
- Malcolm thinks that Macbeth is a danger.

Page 8: Act Three — Scene 1

1. a) False: "Why, by the verities on thee made good" (lines 8-9).
   b) True: "But hush! No more." (line 10)
2. The statements should be numbered 2, 4, 1, 6, 3, 5.
3. "Here's our chief guest." (line 11)
4. Macbeth manipulates them into believing that Banquo has ruined their lives by holding them "under fortune". Macbeth also questions their masculinity, suggesting they'll be "i' the worst rank of manhood" if they won't kill Banquo.
5. He has friends in common with Banquo and he doesn't want them to abandon him.

Page 9: Act Three — Scenes 2 and 3

1. E.g. He wants to protect Lady Macbeth from the guilt caused by killing more people. / He is so driven by his own ambition that he thinks his wife's opinion is unimportant.
2. a) E.g. "our desire is got without content" (line 5).
   b) E.g. "nothing / Can touch him further" (lines 25-26).
3. E.g. The murderers are at risk of being seen as most of Macbeth's nobles are at the palace when Banquo is killed.
4. E.g. "The west yet glimmers with some streaks of day" (line 5). Banquo's murder is an act of darkness. The sunset symbolises another light being extinguished.
5. The Witches prophesied that Banquo's descendents will become king. The fact that Fleance is still alive makes him a threat to Macbeth.

Answers

Page 10: Act Three — Scene 4

1. The statements should be numbered 3, 1, 5, 2, 4.
2. a) He is alarmed when he sees the ghost and initially thinks that the thanes are trying to trick him. He then begins to panic and challenges it to a duel.
   b) His panic could be caused by his guilt and his fear that his role in Banquo's murder will be discovered.
3. She questions Macbeth's masculinity to make him see that his fear is making him look weak. She then asks the other lords to leave to prevent them from becoming suspicious.
4. a) "blood will have blood." (line 122)
   b) "I will — to the weïrd sisters. / More shall they speak." (lines 132-133)
   c) "For mine own good, / All causes shall give way." (lines 135-136)

Page 11: Act Three — Scenes 5 and 6

1. E.g. Hecate tries to control the Witches. She angrily scolds them for interfering in Macbeth's life without her.
2. She will summon apparitions to trick Macbeth into thinking he can control his own destiny, making him over-confident.
3. It shows how many people are affected by Macbeth's reign.
4. Lennox uses sarcasm when he says that Duncan's death "did grieve Macbeth!" He says that Macbeth's murder of Duncan's servants was "wisely" done, showing that he thinks Macbeth was trying to hide something.
5. Malcolm: He is being sheltered at the English court and he has been given a warm welcome.
   Macduff: He is visiting King Edward in England and trying to raise an army to fight Macbeth.

Task: You should have made a flowchart with arrows and labels. Here are some links you may have made:
- The Witches' prophecy that Macbeth will become king causes him to kill Duncan. Duncan's murder causes Malcolm and Donalbain to flee, which makes the thanes suspect them of Duncan's murder.
- The Witches' prophecy that Banquo's sons will be kings causes Macbeth to arrange Banquo's murder. Banquo's murder angers Hecate and causes Lennox to suspect Macbeth. This makes him support Macduff's revolt.
- Macbeth's actions in response to the prophecies anger Hecate, so she decides to trick him with the apparitions.

Page 12: Act Four — Scene 1

1. The list of horrible ingredients creates a dark tone, which hints that something bad is going to happen. This increases the tension.
2. She is pleased with them because they have followed her orders and made an effort to brew the potion.
3. It suggests that he is evil, as even the Witches think that he has become a "wicked" person since they last saw him.
4. a) It tells him to be wary of Macduff — it confirms his fears that Macduff is a threat.
   b) Nobody born from a woman can harm Macbeth — he realises that he doesn't need to fear Macduff because he believes no one can harm him.
   c) Macbeth will never be defeated unless Birnam Wood moves to Dunsinane Castle — he says this is impossible but questions whether Banquo's heirs are a threat.
5. It makes him fearful as it reminds him that Banquo's sons are destined to be kings and his power is therefore limited.

Page 13: Act Four — Scene 2

1. The audience knows that Macbeth is planning to kill Macduff's family and is waiting for it to happen.
2. a) "He loves us not: / He wants the natural touch" (lines 8-9).
   b) "Things at the worst will cease" (line 24)
3. questions, traitors, husband, tease, close
   (Other answers are also possible.)
4. Initially, she thinks about fleeing. She also sees it as proof that she is in the "earthly world" where evil deeds are committed against good people.
5. The First Murderer calls Macduff's son "egg" and "fry", showing that he is very young. This makes his murder seem more shocking. The fact that his murder takes place onstage makes it seem even more brutal.

Page 14: Act Four — Scene 3

1. The statements should be numbered 6, 5, 2, 1, 4, 3.
2. E.g. He thinks Macduff might be loyal to Macbeth, since Macduff has "loved him well". / He thinks Macduff would be rewarded for betraying him by offering "up a weak, poor, innocent lamb / To appease an angry god." / He is suspicious of Macduff because he left his "wife and child" in "rawness" (unprotected).
3. a) Rosse — Good people keep dying under Macbeth's rule.
   b) Macduff — He's wondering whether God watched his family die and did nothing.
   c) Malcolm — Macduff should use his grief to make him stronger.
4. He becomes more determined to defeat Macbeth because he wants to get revenge for the death of his family.

Task: Here are some points you may have included:
- The Witches' prophecy that Macbeth will be king makes him feel entitled to the crown, fuelling his ambition.
- The Witches' prophecy that Banquo's descendants will be kings makes Macbeth feel insecure, causing him to behave ruthlessly when he orders Banquo's murder.
- Macbeth becomes paranoid after Duncan's murder as he is worried that his crimes will be revealed.
- After Macduff betrays him, Macbeth becomes less cautious and kills Macduff's family without hesitation.

Page 15: Act Five — Scenes 1 and 2

1. E.g. She is afraid of the dark and demands that a candle be "by her continually", whereas before she invited "thick night" to hide her evil deeds. She can no longer control her speech or actions.
2. There's no-one to confirm what she says.
3. Committing sins against nature has a strange effect on the mind. People with dark secrets often reveal the truth while sleeping.
4. To remind the audience that Macbeth will be defeated if Birnam Wood comes to Dunsinane.
5. a) True: e.g. "Some say he's mad" (line 13).
   b) False: "Now does he feel his title / Hang loose about him" (lines 20-21).

Page 16: Act Five — Scenes 3, 4 and 5

1. Macbeth claims that he is "sick at heart", which suggests that he is not confident of victory. He seems mad when he asks Seyton to help him put his armour on and then tells him to "Pull't off" again. This suggests that his mind is troubled.
2. He shows the audience that Macbeth is more out of control than earlier in the play. Shakespeare contrasts Malcolm's calm preparation for battle with Macbeth's frantic behaviour.
3. "But certain issue strokes must arbitrate" (line 20).
4. He doesn't seem to grieve. He says that life is short and feels as though human actions are meaningless.
5. "here let them lie / Till famine and the ague eat them up" (lines 3-4).
   E.g. "a wood / Comes toward Dunsinane" (lines 45-46). Macbeth is tired of living and is resigned to his death.

Page 17: Act Five — Scenes 6 to 9

1. a) False: e.g. "Make all our trumpets speak" (Scene 6, line 9).
   b) False: "The tyrant's people on both sides do fight" (Scene 7, line 25).
   c) True: "I bear a charmèd life" (Scene 8, line 12).
2. "But get thee back, my soul is too much charged / With blood of thine already" (lines 5-6).
   E.g. He realises that he has the blood of Macduff's family on his hands and he doesn't want to dishonour himself further.
3. He is concerned for those who died in battle. He promotes his loyal thanes to earls.
4. They both involve a rightful king fighting rebels — Duncan fights the thanes in Act 1, while Malcolm fights Macbeth in

Answers

Act 5. Both times, traitors are killed; the original Thane of Cawdor in Act 1 and Macbeth in Act 5. Loyal men are promoted, with Macbeth being made Thane of Cawdor in Act 1 and the thanes being made earls in Act 5.

Task: Here are some events you may have included:
- Act 1: e.g. Macbeth meets the Witches / Macbeth becomes Thane of Cawdor / The Macbeths plot to kill Duncan.
- Act 2: e.g. Macbeth kills Duncan / Malcolm flees to England / Macbeth becomes king.
- Act 3: e.g. Banquo is murdered / Hecate decides to trick Macbeth / Lennox becomes suspicious.
- Act 4: e.g. The Witches trick Macbeth with apparitions / Macduff's family is killed / Macduff joins Malcolm.
- Act 5: e.g. Lady Macbeth commits suicide / Macbeth faces Macduff / Macbeth is killed / Malcolm becomes king.

Page 18: Skills Focus — Using Quotes

1. true, true, false, false, false
2. Lady Macbeth says that Macbeth is "too full o'th'milk of human kindness" to kill Duncan.
   Macbeth acted "Like valour's minion" in the battle against the Norwegians.
   Lady Macduff thinks her husband's decision to leave was "madness".
   Lady Macbeth's "thick-coming fancies" are tormenting her.

Page 19: Skills Focus — P.E.E.D.

1. a) The Explain stage is missing.
   b) The Develop stage is missing.
2. a) E.g. Shakespeare gives the Witches a masculine feature to make them seem more evil.
   b) E.g. In Act 2, Scene 4, he claims "There's daggers in men's smiles".

Section Two — Characters

Pages 20-21: Macbeth

1. a) "brave Macbeth — well he deserves that name" (Act 1, Scene 2, line 16).
   b) "Hang those that talk of fear" (Act 5, Scene 3, line 37).
   c) "why do I yield to that suggestion, / Whose horrid image doth unfix my hair" (Act 1, Scene 3, lines 134-135).
2. Portraying him as a brave warrior at the start of the play makes his downfall seem even more dramatic. At the end of the play, he regains his bravery before he dies which reminds the audience that he isn't wholly bad.
3. Shakespeare uses a soliloquy to show that Macbeth has doubts about killing Duncan in Act 1, Scene 7. In this soliloquy, Macbeth says that he should "shut the door" against Duncan's murderer, "Not bear the knife" himself.
4. E.g. "Banquo, thy soul's flight, / If it find heaven, must find it out tonight." (Act 3, Scene 1, lines 139-140)
   Any valid explanation, e.g. In Act 1, the idea of killing Duncan horrifies Macbeth. By Act 3, Macbeth doesn't hesitate to order Banquo's death.
5. true, false, true, false, false
6. E.g. Macbeth's feeling that life is fleeting and meaningless gives the impression he is resigned to his fate. The idea that his life is "told by an idiot" suggests that he has no control over his life, which makes him appear weak.
7. E.g. "When you durst do it, then you were a man." (Act 1, Scene 7, line 49)
   Any valid explanation, e.g. Macbeth doesn't want to be seen as unmanly and cowardly so he feels under pressure to kill Duncan.
8. E.g. His ambition, because the Witches don't tell Macbeth to murder anyone. Macbeth chooses to act on their prophecies to fulfil his own ambition; he says the only thing which spurs him on is his "vaulting ambition". **Or** e.g. The Witches' prophecies, because the Witches make Macbeth feel insecure about his future by confusing him with their predictions. Their interference makes him consider killing Duncan before Lady Macbeth does.

Task: Here are some examples you may have included:
- Impulsiveness — e.g. Macbeth shows impulsiveness after seeing Banquo's ghost when he resolves to act on his thoughts "ere they may be scanned".
- Overconfidence — e.g. He displays over-confidence when he claims that he has "a charmèd life, which must not yield / To one of woman born".
- Cruelty — e.g. His cruelty is shown when he shouts at his servant, calling him "Thou lily-livered boy" in Act 5.

Pages 22-23: Lady Macbeth

1. b) She is cleverer and perhaps more ambitious than Macbeth.
   c) She isn't as ruthless as she seems.
   d) She takes control of situations and thinks quickly.
   e) She has become so powerless that her death isn't a key part of the plot.
2. Lady Macbeth uses imperatives like "Come, you spirits" which makes her sound as if she is in control. She also uses dark imagery, asking to be covered "in the dunnest smoke of hell", making her seem terrifying and evil.
3. a) E.g. Meaning: Duncan will be asleep, so we'll be able to do anything that we like.
   Explanation: This suggests that Lady Macbeth feels confident that the plan to kill Duncan will succeed.
   b) E.g. Meaning: I am just as guilty as you, but I'd be ashamed if I were as cowardly as you.
   Explanation: This suggests that Lady Macbeth accepts her role in Duncan's murder, but thinks Macbeth is cowardly for allowing his guilt to make him fearful.
4. a) She seems distressed before Macbeth arrives. She says that her "desire is got without content", suggesting that she is uneasy about the situation. When Macbeth arrives, the tone of her speech changes instantly. She speaks brightly, greeting Macbeth with a cheery "How now, my lord!"
   b) She wants to hide her own feelings from Macbeth to appear strong and to reassure him.
5. E.g. "fill me from the crown to the toe topfull / Of direst cruelty" (Act 1, Scene 5, lines 41-42) / "I'll gild the faces of the grooms withal, / For it must seem their guilt" (Act 2, Scene 2, lines 56-57).
6. At first, she isn't affected by guilt. However, she becomes increasingly tortured by her guilty conscience. Eventually, guilt overwhelms her and contributes to her suicide.
7. Lady Macbeth is more ambitious — e.g. She is willing to kill her own child and to "unsex" herself to get what she wants. She is the one that drives Macbeth to kill Duncan. **Or** Lady Macbeth is less ambitious — e.g. Unlike Macbeth, she is unable to kill Duncan herself, showing that her ambition is not strong enough to overcome her conscience.

Exam Practice:

Your answer should have an introduction, several paragraphs developing different ideas and a conclusion.
You may have covered some of the following points:
- In this extract, Shakespeare shows that Lady Macbeth is afraid of being punished for her crimes. He reveals her troubled thoughts using rambling speech, such as "Hell is murky! Fie, my lord, fie! A soldier, and afeard?" The phrase "Hell is murky" creates a dark image of hell, suggesting that Lady Macbeth feels threatened by the idea that she might be punished in hell for her evil deeds after she dies. Shakespeare uses her language in this speech to reveal her true thoughts to the audience, which might encourage them to pity her.
- In the play, Shakespeare uses conversations between Macbeth and Lady Macbeth to reveal her anxiety about Macbeth's behaviour. In Act 3, Scene 4, she asks Macbeth "Are you a man?" out of fear that he will give them away. Here, Lady Macbeth draws strength from her fear, as it prompts her to take control by directly challenging Macbeth. Her behaviour suggests that their gender roles are reversed, as women in her time normally had limited influence over their husbands' actions.

Answers

• Shakespeare uses sentence structure in the play to reveal the extent of the Macbeths' anxiety just after Duncan's murder. During a rapid exchange, the Macbeths ask each other a series of questions that receive monosyllabic responses like "When?" and "Ay." and finish each other's sentences, instead of speaking in full lines. This creates a fast pace which gives the scene a feeling of nervous energy. This speech contrasts with Lady Macbeth's calm and rhythmic speech in Act 1, emphasising her anxiety in this scene.

Page 24: Duncan

1. a) True: E.g. "More is thy due than more than all can pay" (Act 1, Scene 4, line 21)
   b) False: E.g. "There's no art / To find the mind's construction in the face" (Act 1, Scene 4, lines 11-12)
2. E.g. "Thy royal father / Was a most sainted king" (Act 4, Scene 3, lines 108-109) / "his virtues / Will plead like angels" (Act 1, Scene 7, lines 18-19) / "The service and the loyalty I owe, / In doing it, pays itself." (Act 1, Scene 4, lines 22-23)
3. He nurtures his subjects and is generous to those who serve under him, which shows that he is a caring person.
4. E.g. He is thankful for the soldiers' service to him when he says their "due" is greater than he "can pay". His use of language related to trade makes him seem honourable because it suggests that he recognises that he cannot take his soldiers' loyalty for granted and must reward them fairly.

Task: E.g. Duncan's "absolute trust" in the original Thane of Cawdor leaves him vulnerable to rebellion. Similarly, Duncan's trust in Macbeth makes him blind to Macbeth's ambition and his evil intentions. His trust in the Macbeths also leaves him open to attack when he is at their castle.

Page 25: Malcolm and Donalbain

1. He knows that those around him are being friendly and supportive, but that underneath they are plotting to harm him and Malcolm.
2. Advantage: They will avoid being killed by Macbeth. / They can plan what to do next in safety.
   Disadvantage: Fleeing from the scene makes them look guilty. / Macbeth might be able to plot against them more easily.
3. E.g. Malcolm shows he is good at tactics when he tells the soldiers to cut down branches to disguise themselves. He gives clear orders, and is clearly respected by his men.
4. They are both respected by the Scottish lords. Both are fair and generous, rewarding those who are loyal to them. However, Malcolm is more suspicious of others and puts his trust in the right people, whereas Duncan trusts too easily and is betrayed.

Page 26: Banquo

1. a) Banquo wants to keep his conscience clear when Macbeth offers to reward him for his loyalty in Act 2, Scene 1.
   b) Banquo shows good judgement in his decision not to be swayed by the Witches' prophecies.
2. Although he doesn't trust the Witches at first, he later hopes their predictions will come true. He wonders whether he should have "hope" in the prophecies about him, since the ones about Macbeth have been "made good".
3. E.g. It's as if he is replacing Macbeth. It reminds the audience that his sons are destined to be kings instead of Macbeth's.
4. It makes Banquo seem more honourable because he doesn't give in to his sense of ambition as Macbeth does.

Task: You should have written the questions as if you were an interviewer and the responses from Banquo's ghost's point of view. Here are some points you might have included:
- If you asked why he continued to trust Macbeth despite being suspicious of him, he might have said that he didn't think that Macbeth posed a threat to him personally.
- If you asked why Banquo didn't act on the prophecies, he might have said that his honour and his loyalty to Duncan and Macbeth were more important than his ambition.
- If you asked why he refused to trust the Witches, he may have said that he thought they were trying to trick him. He was wary of the power of the supernatural, so wasn't swayed by the Witches.

Page 27: The Macduffs

1. b) E.g. Macduff is loyal to Scotland.
   c) E.g. Lady Macduff is courageous.
2. Macduff's loyalty to Scotland is strong. He's not willing to support Malcolm if he's going to rule just as badly as Macbeth.
3. E.g. Macduff's son stands up to the "shag-haired villain" who calls his father a traitor. After being stabbed, he bravely tells his mother to "run away" and save herself.
4. E.g. Both are brave heroes at some point in the play; Macbeth is brave at the beginning and Macduff is brave at the end. Macbeth only wants to be king for his own personal gain, whereas Macduff is loyal to Scotland and seeks power for Malcolm, the rightful heir.

Task: Here are some points you could have included if you think Macduff does the right thing:
- Macduff doesn't stand by and allow Macbeth to rule with cruelty. He refuses to obey Macbeth, whose reign is making "New widows howl, new orphans cry" and acts to stop him.
- If Macduff hadn't put his country first and gone to join Malcolm, he may not have ended up facing Macbeth on the battlefield. His decision to leave his family puts him in the position to do the right thing and kill Macbeth.

Here are some points you could have included if you think Macduff does the wrong thing:
- Even though Macduff knows that women and children are suffering under Macbeth's reign, he still leaves his family defenceless.
- If Macduff had stayed with his family, he might have been able to protect them from the murderers. He makes the wrong decision when he leaves them without protection.

Page 28: The Witches

1. a) E.g. "I'll drain him dry as hay" (Act 1, Scene 3, line 17).
   b) E.g. "look not like th'inhabitants o'th'earth, / And yet are on't" (Act 1, Scene 3, lines 40-41).
   c) E.g. "Tell me, if your art / Can tell so much, shall Banquo's issue ever / Reign". (Act 4, Scene 1, lines 100-102).
2. It makes their gender more unclear. This hints to the audience that they are not what they appear to be.
3. Hecate speaks in rhyming couplets, creating rhymes such as "spend" and "end". This makes her sound as if she's casting a spell, making her seem unnatural. She gives orders to the Witches, saying "get you gone", which makes her seem commanding.
4. E.g. The wild nature of a heath reflects the wild nature of the Witches and suggests that they're separated from the rest of society.

Task: Here are some points you may have included:
- In extract: the Witches enjoy their supernatural power
  - Witches dance around cauldron, singing a song, "*Black spirits*" — "And now about the cauldron sing"
  - Dancing makes them seem joyful, revelling in magic.
  - Encourages audience fear them more — happy to cause chaos, no conscience = Witches seem more dangerous.
- In play: the Witches withhold important information
  - Witches are deliberately unclear when speaking — Macbeth calls them "imperfect speakers".
  - Take advantage of their knowledge to mislead Macbeth.
  - Shakespeare creates suspense in scenes when Macbeth acts on Witches' words — audience and Macbeth don't have enough information to know if Macbeth is making a mistake / doing the right thing.
- In play: Witches are part of a bigger supernatural world
  - Hecate scolds Witches, gives orders to them — they "make haste" to obey.
  - Witches answer to a more powerful supernatural being (Hecate), are part of a bigger network of power.
  - Would have made them even more frightening to a 17th-century audience that already believed in witchcraft.

Answers

Page 29: Other Characters

1. It suggests that Macbeth is the devil, as people entering his castle are passing through the gates of hell.
2. The previous two scenes, in which Duncan's murder is planned and carried out, are dark and tense. The Porter's language and behaviour provides comic relief, which lightens the mood.
3. a) He feels that Macbeth's reign is damaging Scotland. Scotland now seems to be dominated by death. E.g. "It cannot / Be called our mother, but our grave". (Act 4, Scene 3, lines 165-166)
   b) He thinks that Malcolm is the one who deserves his loyalty and hopes that Malcolm can heal Scotland by defeating Macbeth. E.g. "Well, march we on, / To give obedience where 'tis truly owed." (Act 5, Scene 2, lines 25-26)
4. Young Siward's dialogue with Macbeth shows the audience just how hated Macbeth has become — his enemies are willing to die to defeat him.

Page 30: Skills Focus — Making Links

1. Here are some examples you could have used:
   Macbeth — He is reliant on Lady Macbeth. / He is more decisive and no longer needs Lady Macbeth's advice.
   Lady Macbeth — She commanding when she convinces Macbeth to kill Duncan. / She has lost control of her mind and desperately "rubs her hands" to wash away her guilt.
2. Here are some examples you could have used:
   Malcolm — cautious. "Our separated fortune / Shall keep us both the safer." / He tests Macduff's loyalty.
   The Witches — evil. The Witches are excited by idea of stopping the sailor from sleeping. / They brew a horrible potion that includes a "birth-strangled" baby's .
   Banquo — noble. "Noble Banquo, / That hast no less deserved". / Banquo does not give in to the temptation of the Witches' prophecies.
   Macduff — brave. Macduff keeps fighting Macbeth even when he says he is unbeatable. / Macduff fights and kills Macbeth to protect Scotland from tyranny.

Page 31: Practice Questions

Your answers should have an introduction, several paragraphs developing different ideas and a conclusion. You may have covered some of the following points:

1.
   - In this extract, Lady Macbeth is shown to be an evil character through the rejection of her maternal role. She says she would have "dashed the brains out" of her own child while breastfeeding. This graphic image shows her to be heartless, especially since the imagined victim is an innocent child. This would have made her seem particularly evil to a 17th-century audience, as women were expected to conform to much stricter maternal roles.
   - Lady Macbeth's manipulation of Macbeth in this extract makes her seem evil. Lady Macbeth uses a conditional sentence, "When you durst do it, then you were a man", to manipulate Macbeth into going against his conscience. This makes her seem evil, as she encourages Macbeth to reject his morality and commit an evil act. This shifts the blame for Duncan's murder onto Lady Macbeth, making her seem more evil.
   - Lady Macbeth is shown to be malicious in the play through her plot to make Duncan's servants appear guilty of his murder. During Act 2, Scene 2, she covers the "sleepy grooms" with Duncan's blood. By describing them as "sleepy", Shakespeare emphasises the fact that the servants are defenceless, which makes Lady Macbeth's plan to take advantage of them seem evil. This is the only time where Lady Macbeth actually carries out an evil act herself, which makes her seem particularly evil at this point in the play.
2.
   - Shakespeare uses an aside to present Duncan as too trusting in this extract. In this aside, Macbeth reveals his true intentions when he contemplates betraying Duncan. Immediately after this, Duncan calls Macbeth a "peerless kinsman". The fact that Macbeth's disloyalty and Duncan's trust in him are shown onstage at the same time highlights the idea that Duncan's trust in Macbeth is misplaced. This warns the audience that those who trust too freely leave themselves vulnerable to betrayal.
   - In this extract, Duncan is presented as a gentle character who doesn't hide his emotions. He personifies his tears when he tells his men that his "plenteous joys" are hiding in "drops of sorrow", meaning that he is crying with happiness in front of his subjects. Duncan therefore shows that he is not afraid to appear emotional, a quality that was not associated with manliness in Shakespeare's time. Duncan is not the only man who shows emotion and is presented positively; Macduff openly grieves for his family in Act 4.
   - Shakespeare presents Duncan as a rightful king throughout the play. After his death, Macduff remembers him as "a most sainted king". Macduff's use of the word "sainted" reminds the audience that Duncan had a divine right to rule. In the 17th century, it was widely believed that kings were chosen by God, so a 17th-century audience would have considered Duncan to be a rightful king. Presenting Duncan as a rightful king would have made Macbeth's claim to the throne seem even weaker.
3.
   - Macbeth's state of mind changes rapidly in this extract. At first, he claims that his heart will "never sag with doubt", but later in the extract he is starting to despair, saying he is "sick at heart". By making Macbeth link his state of mind to his heart, Shakespeare shows how deeply Macbeth's loss of confidence is affecting him. Shakespeare uses Macbeth's increasing doubt to create tension, as the audience knows that his confidence in the prophecies is misplaced and wonders whether Macbeth will realise this before it is too late.
   - In the play, Macbeth struggles with sleeplessness after murdering Duncan. He confides in Lady Macbeth that he is unable to sleep soundly because he is tormented by "terrible dreams / That shake us nightly". Throughout the play, Shakespeare associates disturbed sleep with an unsettled mind, so Macbeth's nightmares show that he is tormented by guilt after killing Duncan. This reinforces the message that those who commit treason, which was considered to be a serious crime in the 17th century, will not escape its consequences.
   - Shakespeare uses Lady Macbeth to highlight Macbeth's fear in the play. During the banquet, Lady Macbeth refers to the "air-drawn" dagger and to Banquo's ghost as "the very painting" of Macbeth's fear. This use of language related to art suggests that Macbeth's insecurity comes from artificial things that his mind has invented. The contrast between Macbeth's fear of imaginary things in this scene and his bravery in Act 1, Scene 2 emphasises how much Macbeth's state of mind changes.
4. a)
   - Macbeth is presented as confident in this scene. He tells Macduff that he bears "a charmèd life, which must not yield / To one of woman born". Macbeth's use of "must", a strong modal verb, makes him seem certain, which shows that he believes wholeheartedly in this prophecy. Earlier in Act 5, the audience learns that the Witches' prophecy about Birnam Wood moving towards Dunsinane has come true, which hints to the audience that his confidence in his safety is misplaced.
   - Macbeth's refusal to surrender to Macduff in this scene makes him seem courageous. He claims that he will fight Macduff, despite the fact that Macduff is "of no woman born" and can therefore kill him. This shows that Macbeth is brave enough to try and defy the Witches' prophecy, even though most of the others have come true. Shakespeare uses this determination to link back to the brave warrior Macbeth was in Act 1, encouraging them to view him with slightly more pity before his death.
   - Macbeth is presented as proud in this extract. He claims that he "will not yield, / To kiss the ground before young Malcolm's feet". In the 17th century, kissing the ground before a king was a way of acknowledging that monarch's superior status. This makes Macbeth seem proud as it suggests that he would rather die in battle than surrender to Macduff and accept Malcolm's superiority. This could encourage the audience to view Macbeth with more respect, as he sticks to his principles.

Answers

b) • In Act 1, Scene 3, the Witches manipulate Macbeth by setting up a self-fulfilling prophecy, a prophecy that comes true as a result of a person's own actions after hearing it. They confuse Macbeth by hailing him "Thane of Cawdor" and "king hereafter" without explaining how he will become king, and then "*vanish*" from the stage, making Macbeth feel unsure about his future. In response, Macbeth commits Duncan's murder so he can secure the throne. The Witches continue to influence Macbeth until Act 5, Scene 8, when Macbeth finally realises that they have been manipulating him.

- Shakespeare uses the play's structure to show that manipulation can influence a character's actions over a long period of time. In Act 1, Scene 7, Lady Macbeth manipulates Macbeth by questioning his masculinity, saying that he will be "so much more the man" if he kills Duncan. Macbeth then uses the same tactic when convincing the murderers to kill Banquo and Fleance, which shows that Lady Macbeth's manipulation is still influencing Macbeth at the start of Act 3. This reinforces the suggestion that Lady Macbeth is the root of evil and that Macbeth is the victim of her manipulation.
- The murderers become victims of Macbeth's manipulation later in the play. In Act 3, Scene 1, Macbeth uses rhetorical questions to convince the murderers that Banquo is their enemy. As a result, they agree to murder both Banquo and Fleance. In the 17th century, subjects were expected to show automatic loyalty to the monarch, so the fact that Macbeth resorts to manipulation to make the murderers carry out his will suggests to the audience that he is a weak king.

Section Three — Context and Themes

Page 32: Ambition

1. a) Macbeth believes that he must overcome obstacles, like Malcolm being the rightful heir, to achieve his ambition of being king.
   b) Macbeth is upset that his heirs won't be kings, suggesting that he is disappointed that his ambition has been limited.
2. It means betraying Duncan, and Macbeth believes he owes Duncan loyalty as his "kinsman and his subject".
3. E.g. Malcolm's ambition to be king puts an end to Macbeth's tyranny. / Banquo's ambition is for his heirs and is therefore unselfish.
4. E.g. Macbeth's ambition to become king leads him to kill Duncan. After this point, he can't escape his tragic fate.

Task: Here are some points you may have included:

- Macbeth's ambition = his 'fatal flaw'
  - "Vaulting ambition which o'erleaps itself / And falls".
  - Macbeth's ambition drives tragic plot: Macbeth kills Duncan (turning point), commits evil to keep throne (tragic consequences), Macduff kills Macbeth (downfall).
  - Lady Macbeth similarity — consequences of ambition = madness, suicide. Pursuing ambition causes downfall.
- Ambition has power to overcome conscience
  - Macbeth asks "why do I yield to that suggestion" — he knows it's a "horrid image".
  - Macbeth knows killing is wrong, ambition makes him consider murdering Duncan.
  - Reinforces message that ambition can be dangerous.
- Important to Shakespeare's message that ambition doesn't always corrupt
  - Banquo's ambition: "May they not be my oracles as well, / And set me up in hope?" vs. sense of honour: "still keep / My bosom franchised and allegiance clear".
  - Banquo keeps honour — ambition doesn't corrupt him
  - Selfish/unselfish ambition contrasted — selfish ambition leads to downfall, unselfish ambition doesn't.

Page 33: Loyalty and Betrayal

1. false, true, false, false, true
2. E.g. She flatters Duncan by telling him that he "loads" her house with "honours deep and broad". She uses Duncan's titles to appear loyal, claiming that she serves at "your highness' pleasure".
3. E.g. Like Macbeth, Lady Macbeth owes Duncan loyalty as his subject. However, Duncan rewards Macbeth for his behaviour in the battle, so the audience might think that Macbeth should show him more loyalty in return.
4. E.g. Macdonald is punished for betraying Duncan in Act 1 and Macbeth is punished for his disloyalty in Act 5. This creates a circular structure that suggests that betrayal will eventually be punished.

Task: Here are some points you may have included:

- Macbeth shows loyalty to Lady Macbeth in Act 1 when he supports her in her plan to kill Duncan, even though he has reservations.
- Macbeth is less loyal towards Lady Macbeth from Act 3 onwards, as he excludes her from his plan to kill Banquo.
- Macbeth shows concern about Lady Macbeth in Act 5 when he asks the doctor about her condition, suggesting that his loyalty to her has not completely disappeared.

Page 34: Kingship

1. Malcolm (quote): E.g. "Producing forth the cruel ministers / Of this dead butcher and his fiend-like queen" (Act 5, Scene 9, lines 34-35).
   Duncan (characteristic): E.g. humble / appreciative
   Edward (quote): E.g. "The mere despair of surgery, he cures, / Hanging a golden stamp about their necks". (Act 4, Scene 3, lines 152-153)
2. E.g. It encourages Macbeth to kill Duncan and frame Malcolm and Donalbain so that he can take the throne.
3. Act 3: E.g. "I to your assistance do make love, / Masking the business from the common eye". (Act 3, Scene 1, lines 122-123)
   Act 5: E.g. "Hang those that talk of fear." (Act 5, Scene 3, line 37)
4. Those who fight for Malcolm are presented as holy: Young Siward is "God's soldier". Malcolm says that he will rule "by the grace of Grace", suggesting he will be led by God.

Exam Practice:

Your answer should have an introduction, several paragraphs developing different ideas and a conclusion.
You may have covered some of the following points:

- Shakespeare compares Macbeth and King Edward in this extract to show that Macbeth isn't a rightful king. The English king is referred to as "pious", which links him to God, whereas Macbeth is said to have a "hand accursed". The adjective "accursed" associates him with evil. In the 17th century, the power of a rightful king was considered to come from God. This would have made Macbeth's rule seem less valid to a devout 17th-century audience.
- Throughout the play, Shakespeare presents Macbeth as a bad king using the opinions of other characters. In Act 4, Malcolm accuses Macbeth of being "bloody, / Luxurious, avaricious, false, deceitful". These adjectives summarise behaviour that Macbeth has already shown, which makes Malcolm's accusations seem fair. Shakespeare also uses this technique in Act 5, when he uses the opinions of several minor characters, who judge Macbeth to be a "tyrant", to show how many people have turned against Macbeth because of his bad kingship.
- Shakespeare uses imagery of nature to present rightful kingship. In Act 5, Lennox vows to water "the sovereign flower" and kill the "weeds". In this plant metaphor, Malcolm's right to the throne is highlighted by the word "sovereign", while Macbeth is likened to "weeds" that must killed to make way for the rightful king. This is similar to the way Shakespeare uses a bird metaphor in Act 2 to present Macbeth's actions in having Duncan killed as morally wrong.

Page 35: Good and Evil

1. It makes his downfall seem more dramatic because he has a long way to fall. It also shows that even an honourable person can fall victim to their own ambition.
2. a) He uses an aside.
   b) E.g. "Let not light see my black and deep desires". He doesn't reject his dark thoughts, which implies his morality is weakening.

Answers

3. They all appear to the sound of *"Thunder"*. This wild weather hints that they are threatening. Each apparition also *"Descends"* after speaking, suggesting that they are returning to hell.
4. In the battle, Macbeth is repeatedly called a "tyrant", reminding the audience that he represents evil. Religious imagery symbolises the conflict between good and evil. Macbeth is a "hell-hound", whereas Young Siward is "God's soldier".

Task: Here are some points you may have included:
- Evil men are associated with violent acts. Macbeth orders Banquo's murder and that of Macduff's family.
- Evil women in *Macbeth* use manipulation to achieve their aims. For example, Lady Macbeth vows to manipulate Macbeth into killing Duncan in Act 1, Scene 5. The Witches use prophecies to manipulate Macbeth in Act 1, Scene 3 and Act 4, Scene 1.

Page 36: The Supernatural

1. a) E.g. "How did you dare / To trade and traffic with Macbeth" (Act 3, Scene 5, lines 3-4)
   b) E.g. "Art thou not, fatal vision, sensible / To feeling as to sight?" (Act 2, Scene 1, lines 37-38)
   c) E.g. "Though bladed corn be lodged and trees blown down, / Though castles topple". (Act 4, Scene 1, lines 54-55)
2. a) Banquo's ghost sits *"in Macbeth's place"*, unnoticed by Macbeth at first. This creates tension, as the audience waits to see how Macbeth will react.
   b) Only Macbeth can see Banquo's ghost, suggesting that it is linked to his guilty conscience.
3. The Witches deliberately lead Macbeth astray, implying that witchcraft is a threat. They are linked to the devil, reinforcing the idea that they are dangerous.

Task: You could have covered the following points:
- Lighting would be used to suggest that the moon is glowing strangely.
- There would be a hazy/smoky atmosphere to allow the Witches to be hidden from the audience.
- The scenery would be quite bare with no plants, apart from burnt or dead trees.
- Their clothing would be dark, well-worn and perhaps ragged to make them appear wild.
- The behaviour of the Witches would be changeable to make them seem more dangerous and unpredictable.
- The Witches would match one another's movements to show that they're a united force.

Page 37: Reality and Appearances

1. E.g. The Witches present him with predictions that imply that he is invincible — they suggest that "none of woman born" can hurt him.
2. E.g. "to win us to our harm, / The instruments of darkness tell us truths" (Act 1, Scene 3, lines 123-124)
   E.g. "And make our faces vizards to our hearts, / Disguising what they are." (Act 3, Scene 2, lines 34-35)
3. E.g. Characters who trust in appearances suffer. Duncan's trust in the Macbeths' false loyalty leads to his death. Macbeth's trust in the apparitions is shown to be misguided.
4. E.g. Macduff. In Act 2, Scene 3, he questions why Macbeth killed Duncan's servants, suggesting that he suspects Macbeth's motives.

Task: Here are some quotes you may have chosen:
- "I'll gild the faces of the grooms withal, / For it must seem their guilt." (Act 2, Scene 2, lines 56-57)
- "At once, good night. / Stand not upon the order of your going, / But go at once." (Act 3, Scene 4, lines 118-120)
- "She has spoke what she should not, I am sure of that". (Act 5, Scene 1, lines 42-43)

Page 38: Fate and Free Will

1. E.g. Yes, because Macbeth says that "chance may crown me, / Without my stir", suggesting that he thinks he may still become king even if he doesn't act on the Witches' prophecy.
   Or e.g. No, because he sees Malcolm as a barrier to power that he must "o'erleap", and decides to kill Duncan, showing that he doesn't trust that fate alone will make him king.
2. E.g. Shakespeare doesn't make it clear whether fate or free will is more powerful. The Witches' prophecies make fate seem powerful, but Macbeth makes the decision to kill Duncan on his own.
3. E.g. Macbeth thinks about killing Duncan in Act 1, Scene 7, showing he is in control of his actions. / Macbeth chooses to act on the prophecies about Banquo and Macduff instead of just accepting them.
4. E.g. It suggests that fate is a real force acting on people. It also implies that fate has the power to change events when it is left alone, as Banquo refuses the temptation to act on the Witches' prophecies.

Page 39: Skills Focus — Writing about Context

1. a) The Witches would have been especially terrifying for 17th-century audiences as witchcraft was believed to be real during this period and many people were frightened of witches.
   b) Lady Macbeth's desire to be more masculine would have shocked a 17th-century audience because at the time women were expected to conform to strictly defined roles as dutiful wives, loving mothers and obedient daughters.
2. Piece of context: 2
   Explanation of choice: The P.E.E.D. explanation bullet states that Macbeth loses the respect of his people due to his bad kingship. The second piece of context explains why this would have been significant to Shakespeare's audience.

Page 40: Practice Questions

Your answers should have an introduction, several paragraphs developing different ideas and a conclusion. You may have covered some of the following points:

1.
   - In this extract, Shakespeare makes the vision of the dagger seem powerful by implying that it leads Macbeth towards Duncan's room. Shakespeare uses the verb "marshall'st" to suggest that the dagger actively encourages Macbeth to pursue his evil intentions. By personifying the dagger, Shakespeare suggests that it is in control. The dagger is shown to be even more powerful in the next scene when the audience learns that Macbeth has followed its lead and killed Duncan.
   - Supernatural elements in the play are shown to be powerful through their ability to control nature. Macbeth accuses the Witches of being able to "untie the winds" in Act 4, Scene 1. The word "untie" makes it seem as though the wind is a wild animal that they have the power to contain and release. A 17th-century audience would have found this description of the Witches' power convincing, as they believed that witchcraft was a real and powerful force of evil.
   - In the play, Shakespeare uses rhythm to highlight the power of the supernatural over human minds. After seeing Banquo's ghost in Act 4, Scene 1, Macbeth speaks in short words and disjointed sentences, saying "Why do you show me this? A fourth? Start, eyes!" This disjointed rhythm reflects his disturbed state of mind, while the questions demonstrate his confusion. This echoes the way Banquo and Macbeth continue to ask short questions after the Witches have left in Act 1, Scene 3, suggesting that the supernatural has a lasting influence over characters.
2.
   - Shakespeare suggests that challenging fate has consequences. In this extract, Hecate says she will punish Macbeth for playing with fate by creating an "illusion" with the apparitions that will "draw him on to his confusion". The rhyming pair of words "illusion" and "confusion" emphasises Hecate's intention to ensure that Macbeth will face consequences for his actions and suggests that he won't be able to escape her punishment. This demonstrates to the audience that those who challenge fate will not go unpunished.

Answers

- In the play, Shakespeare uses Macbeth to show that acting on free will is possible. At the end of Act 1, Macbeth claims he is "settled" on killing Duncan in order to take his throne. The word "settled" implies that Macbeth believes he is making an active choice to kill Duncan when he acts to secure the throne. The idea that Macbeth is acting of his own free will is reinforced by Lady Macbeth's belief that he should "catch the nearest way" to becoming king.
- In the play, Shakespeare uses Macbeth's tragic downfall to illustrate the dangers of believing in fate. Just before his death, Macbeth recalls the apparitions' words from Act 4, Scene 1 when he reassures himself that he can't be killed, "Though Birnam wood be come to Dunsinane". By structuring the last act in this way, Shakespeare makes Macbeth's continued belief in the prophecies seem both foolish and dangerous. This idea would have been supported by many people in the 17th century, when it was believed that God, rather than any other supernatural being, should be trusted to control events.

3.
- In this extract, Shakespeare suggests that those who are evil often appear good. Malcolm states that "all things foul would wear the brows of grace, / Yet grace must still look so". This suggests that evil people hide their true nature by adopting false "grace", making it difficult to tell who is truly good. Shakespeare uses the word "foul" to link back to Macbeth's earlier statement "So foul and fair a day I have not seen." This reminds the audience of the way Macbeth hides his evil intentions by appearing to be loyal to Duncan.
- Shakespeare uses imagery of light and darkness in the play to show that good and evil are opposing forces. Lady Macbeth hopes that heaven will not "peep through the blanket of the dark" to stop her from carrying out her plan to kill Duncan. This suggests that the darkness of hell is covering the world and keep out the light of heaven. In the 17th century, when many people feared being sent to hell, the idea that Lady Macbeth wants to keep out the light of heaven would have made her seem particularly evil.
- In the play, Shakespeare uses Macbeth's status as a tragic hero to show that good and evil qualities can exist within the same person. In Act 5, Macbeth refuses to surrender to Macduff even when he knows Macduff will kill him. Macbeth therefore dies honourably, despite the evil he has committed. Even though Macbeth's downfall is inevitable because he gives in to his 'fatal flaw', Shakespeare uses his honourable death to suggest that good will ultimately conquer evil.

4. a)
- In this extract, Shakespeare presents Lady Macduff as a protective mother. She likens herself to a "poor wren" who fights "against the owl". This extended metaphor portrays Lady Macduff as a gentle creature who isn't afraid to fight a more powerful enemy (symbolised by the more formidable owl) to protect her young. Lady Macduff's behaviour contrasts with Lady Macbeth's claim in Act 1 that she would kill her own child, making Lady Macduff seem more protective in comparison.
- Lady Macduff is presented as a betrayed wife in this extract. Shakespeare reveals that Macbeth intends to kill the Macduffs in Act 4, Scene 1, and then shows Lady Macduff questioning her husband's decision to leave "his babes, / His mansion and his titles" behind in the next scene. Shakespeare therefore makes the consequences of Macduff's disloyalty to his wife clear to the audience before they actually happen. This encourages the audience to pity Lady Macduff, as it makes her seem powerless to stop what is about to happen.
- Lady Macduff is presented as powerless in this extract. Rosse encourages Lady Macduff to trust her husband as he "best knows / The fits o' the season". This suggests that, like many women at the time when the play is set, she has no say in her husband's political decisions and must trust that he knows best. Lady Macduff's powerlessness is emphasised by the fact that she doesn't appear anywhere else in the play, meaning that the audience remember her as a powerless victim.

b)
- Shakespeare uses the theme of loyalty and disloyalty in the play to highlight the strength of ambition. In his soliloquy in Act 1, Scene 7, Macbeth recognises that he owes Duncan loyalty as his subject, an idea that would have been supported in Shakespeare's time. He then admits that it is only "Vaulting ambition" that makes him consider betraying this trust. The word "Vaulting" indicates that Macbeth's ambition reaches far beyond his sense of morality. The fact that Macbeth goes on to murder Duncan in Act 2, Scene 2 confirms that Macbeth's ambition is extremely strong.
- Shakespeare uses the structure of the play to reveal characters' disloyal intentions before they are acted upon in order to create tension. Macbeth's potential for disloyalty and his plan to betray Duncan are revealed in Act 1, but Duncan isn't found dead until Act 2. This delay creates tension as it is unclear whether Macbeth will go through with the murder. Later in the play, Shakespeare shortens the time between Macbeth revealing disloyal intentions and the moment when he carries them out, increasing the pace of the play.
- Macbeth's disloyalty to Lady Macbeth contributes to her growing isolation. Macbeth begins to show less loyalty to Lady Macbeth in Act 3, when he tells her to "Be innocent of the knowledge" of his plans. The fact that he no longer treats her as an equal partner shows that his loyalty to her has grown weaker. Shakespeare demonstrates the effect of this disloyalty on Lady Macbeth by excluding her from Act 4 and giving her only one scene in Act 5, showing how much power she loses through Macbeth's disloyalty to her.

Section Four — Shakespeare's Techniques

Pages 41-42: Form and Structure of 'Macbeth'

1. tragedies, character, noble, destroys, weakness
2. E.g. To show the audience that order has been restored to Scotland — the rightful king is ruling again.
3. It makes the audience wonder why the Witches are interested in Macbeth. The fact that they are witches makes the audience apprehensive about their motives.
4. E.g. Duncan's murder. It is when Macbeth's ambition overrules his sense of morality. It also begins a chain of events that lead to Macbeth's downfall.
5. The way the sailor is unable to sleep in the storm foreshadows how Macbeth will become sleepless with worry and guilt due to his actions.
6. It speeds up the pace of the plot towards the end of the play, as it gives the impression that more is happening.
7. Delaying the murder leaves the audience in suspense, wondering if Macbeth will go through with it or not.
8. b) E.g. Will Macbeth's true nature be discovered?
   c) E.g. Will Macduff try to kill Macbeth?
9. a) E.g. Both passages include references to evil spirits.
   b) To show that Macbeth is now becoming more similar to Lady Macbeth as she was presented at the start of the play.

Page 43: Mood and Atmosphere

1. The "*deserted place*" where the Witches meet could be anywhere and seems desolate, which creates a mysterious mood. The stormy weather makes the scene feel ominous.
2. The Porter talks to Macduff about the effects of getting drunk and recalls how he vomited the night before. The crude nature of this topic creates humour.
3. a) E.g. The alliteration emphasises the repeated idea of being trapped and the reference to "doubts" and "fears" creates a tense atmosphere.
   b) E.g. The idea that Banquo's ghost is lacking bone marrow, warmth and "speculation" (sight) is gruesome and gives the scene a chilling atmosphere.
4. E.g. Fanfares are associated with triumph. The first fanfare confirms that Malcolm has reclaimed the throne. The last one confirms that his victory should be celebrated.

Task: E.g. Act 2, Scene 1 — The mood becomes more threatening. Banquo and Fleance discuss the night's unnatural darkness and Macbeth follows the vision of a dagger. The supernatural elements of this scene suggest that disturbing events are about to

Answers

take place.
Act 3, Scene 4 — In this scene, the mood goes from celebratory to fearful. Macbeth begins the scene feeling triumphant that he has removed Banquo as a threat, but then he learns that Fleance has escaped. The fearful mood is increased by the appearance of Banquo's ghost.
Act 4, Scene 2 — There is a light-hearted mood when Lady Macduff is joking with her son, but it becomes tense when they are warned that danger is coming. Their defencelessness increases this tension, as the messenger leaves them and they can't flee.
Act 5, Scene 5 — The purposeful mood of Act 5, Scene 4 becomes more pessimistic in this scene when Macbeth hears that Lady Macbeth has died. The fact that he's starting to become "aweary of the sun" hints that his death is close.

Page 44: Poetry in Shakespeare

1. a) Unrhymed blank verse: e.g. "And oftentimes, to win us to our harm, / The instruments of darkness tell us truths" (Act 1, Scene 3, lines 123-124)
   b) Rhyme: e.g. "Double, double toil and trouble, / Fire burn, and cauldron bubble." (Act 4, Scene 1, lines 10-11)
2. E.g. To emphasise that they are different and unnatural. / To make their speech sound hypnotic. / To make it sound like they are casting a spell.
3. a) E.g. "There, the murderers, / Steeped in the colours of their trade, their daggers / Unmannerly breeched with gore."
   b) E.g. The long words slow down the pace of the dialogue, which focuses the audience's attention on Macbeth's detailed lies.
4. Lady Macbeth uses lots of short words and speaks in prose (normal sentences), which creates a fast and irregular rhythm. This frantic pace suggests she is agitated.

Task: You should have chosen a soliloquy from the play, e.g. Act 1, Scene 5, lines 37-53. This soliloquy suggests that evil is a central part of Lady Macbeth's character. She calls upon the "spirits" to help to fill her with "direst cruelty". This implies that she actively pursues evil. Her reference to the "spirits" also links her to the Witches, who are associated with evil in the play.

Page 45: Puns and Wordplay

1. meaning, funny, entertain, characters'
2. E.g. The fact that "dispatch" also means 'to kill' suggests that Lady Macbeth is fixated on the idea of killing Duncan. This makes her seem dangerous.
3. a) "unruly"
   b) Lennox uses "unruly" (wild, disorderly) to describe the night's weather, but the audience knows that the night has been "unruly" in another way, as Duncan has been murdered.
4. The paradoxes make the audience uncertain about what the Witches really mean, which makes them seem mysterious and untrustworthy.

Pages 46-47: Imagery and Symbolism

1. Metaphor: e.g. "Most sacrilegious murder hath broke ope / The Lord's anointed temple" (Act 2, Scene 3, lines 61-62)
   Saying that Duncan's body was Christ's temple stresses the idea that his rule was chosen by God. This emphasises the sinful nature of his murder.
   Personification: e.g. The image of the castle laughing in the face of its enemies emphasises Macbeth's confidence — he is convinced that the siege will be unsuccessful.
2. "But signs of nobleness, like stars, shall shine / On all deservers" (Act 1, Scene 4, lines 41-42)
   E.g. This suggests that honour will "shine" down upon subjects who have shown loyalty to the King.
3. After Duncan's murder, Rosse says that darkness does "entomb" their surroundings, even though it's daytime. Evil acts are committed at night and Macbeth's evil thoughts are described as "black".
4. E.g. Duncan's horses begin to eat each other. / The earth is "feverous" and "did shake". / An owl kills a falcon.
5. Scotland is described as being "wounded" by Macbeth's rule. As the play progresses, its injuries get worse. This suggests that Macbeth's rule is like a disease.
6. true, true, false, true
7. In Act 5, Scene 1, she imagines that Duncan's blood is on her hands and tries to wash it off. The fact the "damned spot" won't go away shows that she can't get rid of her guilt.
8. a) Violence: In Act 3, Scene 1, Macbeth convinces the murderers to kill Banquo by questioning whether they are manly enough to do it.
   b) Sensitivity: While mourning the death of his family in Act 4, Scene 3, Macduff says he will grieve "as a man".
9. E.g. It symbolises guilt and worry. Macbeth is afraid of nightmares following Duncan's death. Lady Macbeth's guilt is expressed when she relives Duncan's murder and tries wash her hands free of blood in her sleep.

Exam Practice:
Your answer should have an introduction, several paragraphs developing different ideas and a conclusion. You may have included some of the following points:

- Macbeth's cold-hearted attitude in this extract makes him appear evil. When discussing Banquo and Fleance, he says "they are assailable, / Then be thou jocund". The juxtaposition of the words "assailable" and "jocund" emphasises Macbeth's evil nature, as it shows he is able to find cheer in the idea of murder. The sense that Macbeth is evil is reinforced by the dark imagery that dominates his dialogue in this passage; he says the day is "pitiful" and the night is "seeling" (blinding).
- In the play, Macbeth's evil nature is emphasised by the way he treats others savagely. For instance, he orders the murder of Lady Macduff and her children at the end of Act 4, Scene 1. Lady Macduff's statement that she has "done no harm" shows her innocence, which emphasises the cruelty of Macbeth's actions to the audience. Their murder links Macbeth's evil nature to ambition, as his decision to take revenge on Macduff is partly motivated by his fear of losing power.
- The connection between Macbeth and the Witches at the start of the play makes Macbeth seem evil. His first line, "So foul and fair a day I have not seen", reminds the audience of the Witches' statement "Fair is foul, and foul is fair". The way Macbeth unconsciously echoes the Witches' paradoxical language encourages the audience to associate him with them and with the evil they represent. This link would have been particularly effective for a 17th-century audience, who would have believed in witches and identified them with hell.

Page 48: Skills Focus — Working with Extracts

1. In the previous scene, Macbeth hallucinated a dagger. He is about to tell Lady Macbeth that he has killed Duncan.
2. "What hath quenched them hath given me fire" / "the fatal bellman / Which gives the stern'st good-night"
3. The use of short sentences shows that Lady Macbeth is anxious, which creates a tense atmosphere.
4. E.g. In Act 5, Scene 1, the doctor tells a gentlewoman to "Look after her" when she is sleepwalking and hallucinating.

Page 49: Practice Questions

Each answer should have an introduction, several paragraphs developing different ideas and a conclusion. You may have included some of the following points:

1. - The sound effects in this extract help to create tension. The repeated knocking emphasises how long the Porter is taking to open the gate to the castle. This builds tension for the audience, as his slow response delays the discovery of Duncan's body. The Porter's repetition of the word "knock" adds to this tense atmosphere, as it stresses the idea that people are waiting to be let in.
   - Shakespeare uses dark humour in this passage to create tension. The Porter jokes he is the gate-keeper of the underworld and pretends to answer the door "i'th'name of / Beelzebub"(Satan). This imagery of hell creates an unsettling atmosphere, as the audience knows that there is more truth behind the Porter's joke than he realises. This creates tension,

Answers

as the audience is waiting to find out whether Macbeth's part in Duncan's death will be discovered. The tense atmosphere created by the Porter's joke would have been particularly effective for a 17th-century audience, who would have believed in the idea of an afterlife and feared hell.

- Shakespeare uses staging to create tension in the play. In Act 2, Scene 2, Duncan's murder takes place offstage. This distances the audience from the action and makes them witness the event from Lady Macbeth's limited perspective. Macbeth murdering Duncan offstage creates tension, as the audience has to wait for Macbeth's return to find out if he has been successful. This use of staging also heightens the dramatic impact of noises offstage. Macbeth's cry "Who's there? What, ho!" makes the audience wonder if he's been caught.

2.
- Shakespeare uses the nature of the Witches' dialogue to create a sinister atmosphere. Their speech in this extract is written in rhyme, which makes it sound like a chant. This emphasises the fact that they're conjuring a spell and creates a sinister mood. The Witches' sinister presence is reinforced in the play by the fact that they often appear alongside thunder and lightning, which makes them seem menacing.
- The way that nature is corrupted by evil acts in the play creates a sinister atmosphere. After Macbeth murders Duncan, an old man notes the "unnatural" way that "dark night strangles the travelling lamp". The fact that darkness continues into daytime suggests that the natural order has been turned upside down, creating an unsettling atmosphere. The word "strangles" adds to this feeling of unease. It highlights the violent nature of the darkness that has overcome the light of the sun, which is symbolised by the "travelling lamp".
- *Macbeth's* tragic form contributes to its ominous atmosphere. As tragic heroes usually have a 'fatal flaw' that destroys them, the audience wonders from the very start of the play what the nature and the cause of Macbeth's downfall will be. This creates a foreboding mood. 17th-century audiences would have felt the tense atmosphere particularly strongly, as tragedies were a popular form of entertainment in England at the time.

3. a)
- In this extract, Lady Macbeth challenges Macbeth's authority over her. At the start of the extract, Macbeth tells Lady Macbeth "We will proceed no further in this business." The word "will" gives his dialogue a decisive tone that shows he is trying to impose control. However, Lady Macbeth challenges his decision, which suggests that she doesn't recognise his authority. This would have seemed unnatural in 17th-century England, as husbands usually had undisputed authority over their wives.
- Macbeth's decision not to kill Duncan causes conflict with Lady Macbeth in this extract. She questions his choice without letting him reply. Her string of questions suggests that she disagrees with Macbeth on many points, emphasising the conflict between them. The fact that Lady Macbeth's first question shares a line with the end of Macbeth's speech heightens this sense of conflict, as makes it sound as if she has interrupted him and isn't prepared to consider his point.
- In the extract, conflict arises between Macbeth and Lady Macbeth over ambition. Whilst Macbeth maintains that he is content with "Golden opinions", Lady Macbeth desires "the ornament of life" (the crown). Her use of hyperbole (exaggeration) to describe the importance of kingship shows that she considers it to be the ultimate ambition in life and makes Macbeth's "Golden opinions" seem less valuable. This conflict reveals the strength of Lady Macbeth's ambition, which seems greater than Macbeth's at the start of the play.

3. b)
- Ambition is shown to be a corrupting influence through the play's structure. Macbeth begins the play as "brave Macbeth". However, in Act 5, Scene 7, Macduff calls him a "Tyrant". This contrast between the way Macbeth is presented at the start and end of the play highlights how far he has been corrupted by his ambition. This transformation would have seemed dramatic to a 17th-century audience, who would have placed great weight on the noble qualities (like bravery) that Macbeth demonstrates at the start of the play.
- Shakespeare shows that people can have ambition for others, as well as for themselves. In Act 1, Scene 4, Duncan tells Banquo and Macbeth that he has begun to "plant" them and will work to make them "full of growing". This metaphor implies that Duncan has tried to guide Banquo and Macbeth so that they will 'grow' into successful men. This idea is extended by Lennox in Act 5 when he refers to Macbeth as one of Scotland's "weeds", suggesting that Macbeth hasn't become the type of man Duncan was hoping for.
- Shakespeare also suggests that ambition can be positive if it isn't motivated by selfishness. In Act 3, Scene 4, Macduff mourns how Scotland has changed under Macbeth and wishes it could be "wholesome" again. The word "wholesome" suggests that Macduff's ambition to defeat Macbeth is unselfish, as it results from his desire to help Scotland. This positive presentation of ambition is reinforced by Malcolm, who shows his unselfish attitude by maintaining he is "my poor country's to command".

4.
- In the extract, Scotland's future is presented as bleak. Rosse notes that as a result of Macbeth's rule, Scotland is no longer a "mother", but a "grave" instead. This suggests that Scotland should represent new life and growth, but is associated with death under Macbeth's rule. The gloomy atmosphere surrounding Scotland's future in the extract is replicated in Act 5, Scene 3, when Macbeth asks the Doctor to discover Scotland's "disease". This highlights the need for Scotland to be cured before it is too late.
- Scotland is shown to be threatened in this extract and in the play as a whole. The "groans" and "shrieks" of the Scottish people remind the audience of Malcolm's earlier assertion that Scotland "weeps" and "bleeds". Shakespeare's personification of the injured and ill Scotland reminds the audience of the damage Macbeth is inflicting on the country. As Scotland's injuries have been caused by Macbeth's tyrannical rule, Shakespeare encourages the audience to criticise Macbeth.
- Scotland is presented as disordered after Duncan's death, which shows how disruptive tyrants were considered to be in the 17th century. In Act 4, Scene 2, Lady Macduff says that Scotland has become a place where evil actions have become worthy of praise and doing good has become a "dangerous folly." Her implication that the values of good and evil have been reversed shows how Macbeth has disrupted order in Scotland. This idea is emphasised by the play's circular structure, as order is restored to the narrative by the play ending in the same way it began, with the rightful king on the throne.

Section Five — Exam Buster

Page 50: Understanding the Question

1. b) To what extent is Macbeth presented as a strong character in the play?
   c) Explore how the relationship between Macbeth and Lady Macbeth is presented.
   d) How does Shakespeare use the Witches to explore the theme of reality and appearances?
   e) Explain how Shakespeare presents Banquo in the play.
   f) How is the theme of fate and free will presented in the play?
   g) Write about the significance of Duncan in the play.
2. a - 2, b - 1, c - 4, d - 3, e - 5

Page 51: Making a Rough Plan

1. E.g. Lady Macbeth pretends to faint to distract other characters. / The Witches use language to create confusion. / Lady Macbeth is able to disguise her evil at first.
2. Pick your three most important points and put them in a sensible order. Write down a quote or an example from the text to back up each one.

Answers

Page 52: Making Links

1. Lady Macbeth calls Macbeth a "coward".
 Macbeth calls Lady Macbeth "dear wife!"
 E.g. Macbeth doesn't show much emotion when he hears of his wife's death.
2. E.g. If one of your points was 'The Witches use language to create confusion', and your evidence was that the Witches give misleading prophecies such as "none of woman born / Shall harm Macbeth", another example could be that the Witches chant "Fair is foul, and foul is fair", which suggests that things that may seem good are actually evil.

Page 53: Structuring Your Answer

1. Point: Macbeth is troubled by his conscience.
 Example: In Act 1, Scene 7, Macbeth voices his fears about "deep damnation" after death.
 Explain: This suggests that he is aware of the consequences of his actions and knows that he will suffer as a result of killing the King.
 Develop: There is a strong contrast in this scene between Macbeth and Lady Macbeth, who shows no concern or guilt for her actions.
2. a) The Witches call Macbeth "wicked".
 b) Duncan is considered to be a "gracious" king.
3. E.g. Point: Lady Macbeth uses false appearances to hide her evil deeds from other characters.
 Example: In Act 2, she pretends to faint to draw attention away from Macbeth's suspicious behaviour.
 Explain: Lady Macbeth pretends to be shocked, creating a false impression of her reaction to Duncan's murder that covers up her true role in his murder.
 Develop: By Act 5, Lady Macbeth's guilt and madness mean she is no longer able to disguise her evil deeds.

Page 54: Introductions and Conclusions

1. Intro a) is better, e.g. Intro b) discusses the plot of the play rather than focusing on Lady Macbeth, and doesn't cover the 'to what extent' part of the question. It also starts to discuss Macbeth, who isn't mentioned in the question.
2. E.g. The conclusion should focus on Lady Macbeth as ambitious, rather than ruthless. The third sentence shouldn't introduce new ideas and should be more relevant to the question. It should include a judgement about the 'extent' to which Lady Macbeth is presented as ambitious.

Task: Your introduction and conclusion should both give a clear answer to the question. The introduction should include your main points, but no evidence. Your conclusion should summarise your argument and not include new points.

Page 55: Writing about Context

1. a - 1, b - 3, c - 2
2. Contextual information: 17th-century England was very religious so the image of the "serpent" would have made audiences at the time think of Satan taking the form of a snake in the Bible.
3. You could have included context as the Explain or Develop part of the paragraph. The context you wrote about should be relevant to your Point and linked to the Example.

Page 56: Linking Ideas and Paragraphs

1. E.g. Throughout the play, Macbeth is plagued by visions. For example, in Act 2, Scene 1, Macbeth asks, "is this a dagger which I see before me...?" This suggests that Macbeth has begun his descent into madness as he can no longer trust his own judgement. Similarly, Lady Macbeth is presented as mad when she begins to hallucinate a "damned spot" of blood.
2. You should have used the P.E.E.D. structure and included connecting words and phrases such as 'therefore' or 'which shows that' to link your ideas.
3. E.g. Moreover, Shakespeare presents reality and appearances as... / This idea is reinforced by...

Page 57: Marking Answer Extracts

1. 4-5: The answer gives a thoughtful response, but there are some spelling errors. It examines how Shakespeare uses language, but doesn't analyse it closely enough for it to be a 6-7 answer. The answer includes some contextual information, but this information isn't used to explore the relationship between the text and the play's context.

Page 58: Marking Answer Extracts

1. a) 8-9: E.g. "The characters are first introduced... in battle." — arguments supported with well-integrated, precise examples from the text
 "This is highlighted in Act 3, Scene 1... emphasising his determination to suppress his ambition." — close and perceptive analysis of language
 b) 6-7: E.g. "In Act 3, Scene 1... 'royalty of nature'." — integrated, well-chosen examples
 "The word 'treasonous'... a good king." — exploration of the relationship between the text and its context

Pages 59-60: Marking a Whole Answer

1. 8-9: E.g. The answer includes well integrated, precise examples of how Shakespeare uses language, structure and form to convey ideas to the reader. There is a critical discussion of the relationship between the text and its social and historical context. The answer is well-written and uses highly relevant subject terminology.

Page 61: Skills Focus — Writing Well

1. When Macbeth is made Thain *[Thane]* of Cawdor, he realises that the Whiches' *[Witches']* first prediction has come true. This gives him more confidense *[confidence]* in the prophecy that he will be king. He writes a letter about the Witches' predictions to lady macbeth *[Lady Macbeth]*, who begins to devise a plot to kill Duncan and become queen. The urgency of her planing *[planning]* hints at her evil nature.
2. a - 2, b - 1, c - 4, d - 5, e - 3, f - 6

Page 62: Practice Questions

Each answer should have an introduction, several paragraphs developing different ideas and a conclusion. You may have included some of the following points:

1. • In this extract, Macbeth's mind is shown to be weak when he suddenly becomes scared after hearing about Fleance's escape. He says the news about Fleance causes doubt to take over his mind, despite previously claiming to be "Whole as the marble, founded as the rock". These similes highlight Macbeth's new insecurity by contrasting it with his former strength. This change reinforces the idea that as Macbeth's guilt increases, his mind gets weaker.
 • Hallucinations demonstrate the fragility of Macbeth's state of mind later in the play. In Act 3, Scene 4, he becomes distressed by the appearance of Banquo's ghost and claims he is "a man again" once the ghost has disappeared. This suggests that Macbeth's fear of the ghost makes him lose his identity as a man, an idea which would have been familiar to an audience in the 17th century, when masculinity was particularly associated with strength. Hallucinations are also used to establish Macbeth as weak in Act 2; the vision of the dagger encourages Macbeth to overcome his sense of morality and murder Duncan.
 • Shakespeare presents Macbeth as mentally strong in the face of death at the end of the play. In Act 5, Macbeth says he is doomed and "cannot fly", but vows that he will fight in a "bear-like" way. Macbeth's conviction shows that he has mental strength as he is aware of his desperate situation, but is still determined to fight as bravely as a "bear". This reminds the audience of his courage during the battle against the Norwegian army, and partially redeems Macbeth in their eyes.

Answers

2. a) • Arguably, any audience would find it shocking that Macbeth considers committing treason by killing Duncan. In this soliloquy, Macbeth admits that he owes his king protection, saying he should "shut the door" against Duncan's murderer, "Not bear the knife" himself. The fact that Macbeth thinks about killing Duncan while admitting that he should do the opposite highlights how treacherous his thoughts are. Macbeth's ideas seem even more shocking given that the penalty for plotting against the king in the time the play was set was beheading.
• Macbeth's recognition in this extract that Duncan is a good king makes the audience regard his intentions as evil. He admits that "tears shall drown the wind" if Duncan is killed. This imagery reveals how beloved Duncan is by suggesting that grief for him would have the power to "drown" a force as strong as the wind. The fact that the audience has already witnessed Duncan's virtue in Act 1, Scene 2 strengthens the idea that Macbeth is evil for even considering killing him.
• Macbeth's thoughts in this extract highlight the fact that he is a tragic hero, which may make the audience fear for his future. Macbeth suggests that "Vaulting ambition" is the "spur" that is encouraging him to consider killing Duncan. Here, Shakespeare shows that Macbeth is a tragic hero by hinting that "ambition" is his 'fatal flaw'. The fact that a tragic hero can't usually escape his downfall encourages the audience to fear for his safety. Through this presentation of Macbeth as a tragic hero, the audience may conclude that choosing to give in to ambition can have serious consequences.

b) • An audience might feel that Lady Macbeth deserves sympathy when Macbeth stops confiding in her. In Act 3, Macbeth refuses to tell Lady Macbeth what he plans to do about Banquo and dismisses her using the patronising phrase "dearest chuck". This may encourage the audience to pity her, as women in Shakespeare's time were often powerless if their husbands chose to ignore their influence. The fact that Lady Macbeth was shown to be in control of Macbeth in Act 1 makes her loss of power from Act 3 onwards seem even more pitiable.
• Lady Macbeth's overwhelming sense of guilt in Act 5 may provoke sympathy. In Act 5, Scene 1, she says "will these hands ne'er be clean" while reliving the moments after Duncan's death. Lady Macbeth's inability to wash away imaginary blood symbolises the impossibility of washing away her guilt. Her madness and her desperate, repeated handwashing may cause the audience to pity her. Lady Macbeth's vulnerability in this scene contrasts with her ruthless behaviour at the start of the play, making her seem more deserving of pity.
• It could be argued that Lady Macbeth deserves sympathy because she becomes increasingly unimportant to the plot. The play's structure highlights her decreasing importance. In Acts 1 and 2 she influences many of Macbeth's decisions, but she appears less from Act 3 onwards and is entirely absent from the stage in Act 4. Her absence highlights how insignificant she has become to the plot. The audience may feel even more sympathy for her in Act 5 when her suicide takes place offstage, as this suggests that her death is insignificant to the plot.

3. • In this extract, Shakespeare suggests that Malcolm's care not to misplace trust saves him from being betrayed by Macbeth, leaving Malcolm free to oppose him. Malcolm says that wisdom "plucks" him away from "over-credulous haste". Here, Shakespeare uses the verb "plucks" to personify wisdom as a force that physically pulls Malcolm away from believing in the "Devilish" Macbeth, suggesting that Malcolm was at risk of being deceived. This reinforces the idea which was introduced through the murder of Duncan that trusting too easily can have negative consequences.
• Shakespeare uses the play's structure to suggest that Macbeth is endangered by his misplaced trust in the Witches' prophecies. In the scene before his death, Macbeth claims that he laughs "to scorn" weapons wielded "by a man that's of woman born". The rhyming couplet created here echoes the apparitions' advice in Act 4 that he should "laugh to scorn / The power of man" because "none of woman born" can hurt him. This reminds the audience that Macbeth still believes it is true that he is safe from harm. Shakespeare therefore suggests that trusting in the supernatural should be avoided.
• Shakespeare shows throughout the play that uncertainty over who should be trusted can create political turmoil — an idea that would have been familiar to an early 17th-century audience that had just witnessed an attempt to overthrow the king. In Act 4, Scene 2, Rosse claims that, as a result of fear of traitors, Scotland's nobility is being tossed "upon a wild and violent sea". This image reflects the turmoil that the nobility is experiencing under Macbeth's reign. The political turmoil Rosse describes remains until Act 5, Scene 9, when Malcolm, who is presented as a rightful and trustworthy leader, returns to the throne.

4. a) • Lady Macbeth is shown to take control of the situation in the moments after Duncan's murder while Macbeth struggles with his guilt. She orders Macbeth to "Go get some water / And wash this filthy witness from your hand." The use of imperatives like "Go" and "wash" makes Lady Macbeth seem commanding and shows that she is able to stay in control of her emotions. These roles are reversed by the beginning of Act 5. Macbeth takes charge and Lady Macbeth loses control as she descends into madness as a result of her guilt.
• Shakespeare suggests that Macbeth's fear and guilt limit Lady Macbeth's control over him in this extract. Macbeth ignores both her order to smear blood on Duncan's servants and her attempt at emotional manipulation when she scolds him for being "Infirm of purpose". This suggests that Macbeth's fear and guilt are stronger than her manipulation, which shows that she is not in control. Lady Macbeth's inability to control Macbeth reflects the fact that women in her time often had little direct power over their husbands.
• Lady Macbeth tries to control Macbeth's thoughts in this extract. She encourages Macbeth to stop thinking in a "brain-sickly" way about Duncan's murder, which suggests that he is allowing his feeling of guilt to infect his mind. By insulting Macbeth's weak mindset, Lady Macbeth tries to get him to strengthen it. The fact that Macbeth continues to dwell on Duncan's murder until the end of the scene highlights her failure to control his thoughts.

b) • The evil act of murdering Duncan plunges Macbeth into emotional turmoil. In this extract, Macbeth hears a voice say that he "does murder sleep" after killing Duncan. The use of the word "murder" links Macbeth's sleeplessness, which symbolises his guilty conscience, to the act of murdering Duncan. Shakespeare reinforces the idea that evil acts cause sleeplessness in Act 3, Scene 6 when a lord claims that defeating the tyrannical Macbeth will return "sleep to our nights".
• Shakespeare uses structure to show that the evil designs of the Witches influence the events in the play. The Witches appear twice close to the start of the play. This establishes them as a dominant force in the play, as they set the plot in motion by manipulating Macbeth. This reinforces the idea that would have been very familiar to a 17th-century audience that supernatural beings are evil and can cause chaos.
• In the play, Shakespeare associates committing evil acts with paranoia. In Act 3, Scene 4, Macbeth asks his thanes "Which of you have done this?" upon seeing Banquo's ghost. Macbeth has only just received confirmation that Banquo is dead, so it is irrational for him to believe that his thanes are aware of his guilt. This makes him seem paranoid to the audience. Later in the play, Macbeth's paranoia prompts him to order the murder of Macduff's family which suggests that paranoia can be both a cause and a consequence of evil deeds.

The Characters from 'Macbeth'

After all those questions you should now be a *Macbeth* master. Time to reward yourself with a little light relief. Find a comfy chair, put your feet up and feast your eyes on *Macbeth — The Cartoon*...

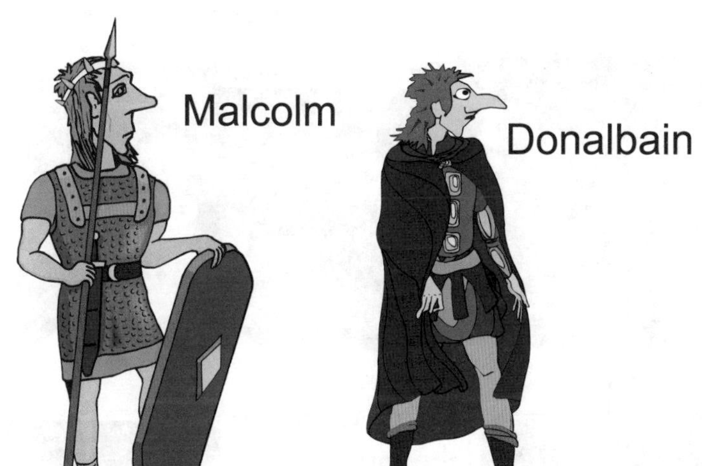

William Shakespeare's 'Macbeth'